3 1336 00157 5548

D0046759

Women and Children

First

SAN DIEGO PUBLIC LIBRARY

BY CADY HEWES

(Bernard DeVoto)

HOUGHTON MIFFLIN COMPANY BOSTON
The Riverside Press Cambridge

1956

COPYRIGHT © 1949, 1950, 1951, 1952, 1953, 1954, 1955 BY BERNARD DEVOTO. ALL RIGHTS RESERVED INCLUDING THE RIGHT TO REPRODUCE THIS BOOK OR PARTS THEREOF IN ANY FORM. LIBRARY OF CONGRESS CATALOGUE CARD NUMBER: 56–1147. FIRST PRINTING NOVEMBER 1956. THE ARTICLES IN THIS BOOK ARE REPRINTED BY PERMISSION OF *Woman's Day* MAGAZINE.

The Riverside Press

CAMBRIDGE · MASSACHUSETTS

PRINTED IN THE U.S.A.

JAN 2 1 '57

Contents

MEET THE HEWESES

1

The World Wives Live In

SOMETHING like twenty years ago a French psychologist published some interesting studies which indicated that the logic of children is entirely different from that of adults. Many of the ideas children hold which seem irrational to grownups, he said, have been reached by a reasoning process that is quite as intelligent as any their parents use but works in entirely different patterns. Much of their behavior that seems unmotivated really proceeds out of severely logical analysis of what the situation of the moment calls for — only it is an entirely different kind of logic. The difference is so great, the psychologist said, that he was forced to conclude that there is a difference between what is real for children and what is real for adults. Growing up means, very largely, growing into an adult's sense of reality. But, quite literally, children live in a different world.

The psychologist died soon after publishing his studies

and at about the same time I got married. I have come to mourn his passing, for the world needed him. It seems possible that he might have gone on to study a system of logic and a sense of reality far more at variance with those of everyday common sense than children's. He might have told us something about the exceedingly strange world of those who have that sense of reality and who reason with that logic. I mean: wives. That is to say: my wife. But if you think my wife isn't every husband's wife, ask any other husband.

What it comes to in the end is that Nancy is an ethical monster, for through nearly twenty years she has lived and cohabited with a complete stranger and has borne him children. The fact that ours is a legal union does not alter her moral guilt in the least, for surely it is depraved to live openly with a man whom you have never met before, whom you have never even looked at or listened to, who every day amazes you by exhibiting something so fixed and fundamental in his nature, habits and point of view that, if he weren't a married man, you would have recognized it instantly while you were being introduced. This shameless immorality is a product of the world wives live in but we had better lead up to it with some study of the logic behind it. That logic, I have come to understand, is rigorous and without fallacy, and it represents the working of a powerful intelligence. But if I had not run into the French psychologist I have mentioned, I should never have known that it is logic.

Nancy lives with this stranger in a suburb of a big city. For many years she has driven to and from the city at least twice a week. A fine express highway goes past our house at a distance of only a couple of blocks. For years Nancy has reached the highway going in, and left it coming back, at a point halfway to town and by a route that takes her through a maze of stop lights, narrow one-way streets and bottlenecks jammed with traffic. Her route converts a ten-minute drive into a twenty-minute drive. Why does she take it? Because it is shorter. In the days when I was still unbowed and eager and coura-geous I repeatedly timed it for her and pointed out the mileage readings on the speedometer. It invariably came out that her route is a couple of miles longer in distance than the highway and twice as long in time. But she sticks to it on logically unassailable grounds. Her route is shorter, she says, and wouldn't it be silly not to take the shortest way?

But that is only logic's first step. When we were coming home one afternoon last fall with Nancy at the wheel, we found the entrance to her route blocked off for some road repairs. She took the boulevard all the way home. As she got out of the car, she said with thoughtful surprise, "You know, it's shorter by the highway." She is no stranger to the man she lives with and if I felt any impulse to com-ment on her discovery I repressed it. She drove the high-way contentedly, and probably with a fine sense of dis-patch and efficiency too, till the paving job was finished, then went back to her habitual route and has used it ever since. I did venture to ask why, having discovered a shorter route, she still used the longer one. I got an an-swer that will surprise no one who has tried to make a map of any part of the world wives live in. Nancy said with candid patience, "Why, isn't it logical to use a way you know?"

There are pleasures which husbands have learned to substitute for uxoricide and I could enjoy one here by saying more about my wife and automobiles. Thus in the hundreds of thousands of miles I have driven since we were married I have never received a parking ticket, been stopped for speeding, dented a fender, run off the road, damaged my car or scraped another car. Nancy's life, on the other hand, is full of such episodes, though she invariably gets out of them by the crassest feminine means — it has never yet taken her sixty seconds to get a policeman on her side. In the course of our marriage she has come to feel a considerable affection for me and so she is deeply worried whenever I drive a car. As an expert driver she envisions what is sure to happen when such a hopeless if well-meaning bungler takes the wheel, and she wishes, and frequently says, that out of consideration for her if nothing else I ought to learn how to drive a car properly. At such moments husbands realize how small and frail a woman's neck is, but we're talking about the world wives live in.

Time and time-relationships in that world are surprising. Concerts and theaters start exactly forty-five minutes before they are due to, I learned long ago, and planes and trains leave exactly sixty minutes ahead of schedule. This has something to do with reading the program at one's leisure and getting comfortably settled in a Pullman, both long processes, but I have a sorrowful fantasy still that sometime the janitor will beat us to the concert hall or the train will be made up when we reach the station. Or iron-hard logic will dictate some such reasoning as this, which I have turned over in my mind hundreds of times without finding out what the gimmick is: we will be going to the Robinsons' for dinner and Nancy will get dressed in furious haste for, "We've got to be there exactly when she said — the Robinsons are always late." But time's most resistant mystery is the aging period of wives' clothes.

Nancy has a very adequate wardrobe and I like it and our friends do too; so, the glances of strangers on the sidewalk assure me, does nearly everyone. But its most striking attribute is that every garment in it is either brand-new or else exactly seven years old. A friend, male or female, will admire a dress, a jacket, a scarf or a pair of shoes, and Nancy will be pleased. But her truest pleasure comes from the eager, wholly honest remark which she immediately makes, "And hasn't it stood up well? (or, Wasn't I lucky the style came back?) I bought it seven years ago." A man's mind, accustomed to a world where days are twenty-four hours long and years have four seasons of three months each, feels under absolute obligation to point out that last October or a year ago last June actually was not seven years ago. Something mad and anarchic is loose in the world, he feels, unless a year means a year and seven equals three plus four. Sense, logic, the foundations of the universe rest on those unshakable truths. So I have many times deeply hurt my wife by trying to hold her to measurements of time which, in her world, hideously falsify the facts. It really was seven years ago she bought that skirt. She remembers with absolute clarity and a wealth of supporting detail, and she has carefully checked the time in between, practically day by day, and seven years is right. She is hurt by my contrariness and she is also disturbed by the evidence that my mind is slipping.

You see, time is relative, it expands and contracts. It keeps a garment new for a season and then, since she bought it long ago, ages it seven years overnight. One plays with the idea of surreptitiously marking the date with indelible ink just inside the hem the next time she buys something. But one never does; insurance rates on married men are high already.

If time is irregular in a wife's world, arithmetic is too. A kindly providence endowed Nancy with the most voracious appetite in North America and deprived her of the ability to convert food into surplus flesh. Her weight has not varied four ounces since we were married and she has no more hips than a pencil. Nevertheless, every so often, the light of inner revelation informs her that she has got fat, and she looks in a mirror and is horrified by evidence invisible to anyone but herself. She must begin to diet and she proceeds to do so with the forthright vigor she brings to all practical affairs. She diets scientifically, by the calorie system as laid out in a book which she keeps in reserve between seizures. That book lists every known kind of food and prints in boldface the calorie-content of every leaf or spoonful. With magnificently stern self-discipline she holds herself absolutely to the precepts set forth in the book — and they are inhuman, they make the rations of a German prison camp seem sybaritic. The book says that a person who is really earnest about losing weight will never consume more than 1200 calories a day — about three-quarters of a moderate lunch. Nancy never exceeds that maximum, however tempted she may be. As a matter of fact, she can't exceed it. There is no way of combining figures in the book so that they will add up to more than 1200.

Sometimes after seeing her put away, say, three enormous slices of roast beef, I have remarked that she has eaten her way well past next Sunday. But she hasn't and, if I persist, she will prove it. This was rare roast beef, she points out, and there are no calories at all in rare roast beef. It does no good to appeal to the book — I ought to realize by now, she says, that she just uses the book for reference, she has all the calories by heart. And it does no good to remark that the beef she has just eaten wasn't so rare at that, for she points out to me that there aren't any calories in beef no matter how it's cooked, everybody knows that. Well, how about the three hot-dog sandwiches she ate at the hockey game last night, I ask. Aren't there any calories in pork, either? This simply evokes the smile of an affectionately indulgent wife: of course there aren't, not the kind of calories that make you fat.

It isn't bright of me not to have got that distinction by now, but Nancy is willing to explain it to me once more: the kind of calories that make you fat are those in fats and sweets and starches, not proteins. (They are exclusively in proteins, however, if she has just eaten squash pie with whipped cream.) Masculine belief in an orderly world is now likely to betray me into making a logical demonstration that will be unanswerable. Look, I say, a calorie is a calorie even if you get it from a piece of coal, and there may be only four calories in a whole head of lettuce, but if you were to eat two thousand heads of lettuce a day you'd get fat. I only give Nancy that familiar blend of tolerant amusement and apprehension that I'm getting old. I couldn't, she says, and wouldn't anybody be a fool to try? With the dauntless stupidity of any fighter in a hopeless cause, I try again. I say: the truth is, you stop counting calories at 1200; you eat whatever you want to, but you disregard calories from there on, you call them out of bounds and say they don't count. You wouldn't, I sum up like an attorney who has proved his case, you wouldn't be able to do that at a bank. You couldn't draw checks up to the amount of your balance and then go on drawing checks on the theory that after that they didn't count. Nancy has now had about as much male irrationality as she can take. We aren't talking about money, she says, we're talking about calories.

We stop talking about them. And a week or so later Nancy puts the book away again and gets calories out of her mind. She has taken off three or five or seven pounds that were never there and she feels happy and well repaid for her sacrifice. She shows me how flat she is in the stomach or directly back of it, and there's no question but that she is as flat in both places as it is decently feminine to be. It would be — well, not so much inconsiderate as injudicious — to say anything except that any man on earth would be proud of her.

Arithmetic also becomes purely relative when Nancy feels like being a helpless little bundle of femininity without mind enough to understand whatever job she wants to unload on her husband. That is, of course, a familiar experience in the world all wives live in. Many a woman cannot balance her checkbook who runs the accounts of a mother's club, the PTA and the League of Women Voters without ever losing track of a penny. Many a woman with an executive talent that would have made her husband rich if he had hired her for the firm instead of marrying her cannot do the administrative detail required to get tickets for the theater or check the estimates for repainting the upstairs. Nancy went much farther with mathematics at college than I did, but it turns out she can't keep figures straight if she has to climb a ladder, make a series of telephone calls or look something up in a book to check her results. Her mind is incapable of grappling with such intensely intellectual matters and she becomes so appealingly feminine, so wistfully mortified by her silliness, that men would rush in droves to prove their virility by doing the job for her if a husband were not enough.

Directions are also wholly relative in Nancy's world. When she makes a long trip by herself she has the mind of an airplane navigator, never hesitates, never goes wrong, never misses a single roadfork. But if I am along she will turn north where she should turn south unless I brief her half a mile in advance, and she cannot even read the route numerals by the roadside. She explains that she is not map-minded, that she simply cannot tell one direction from another or remember where the sun should be, and that it is a great comfort to have a man along to make with instant sagacity the decisions that are so far beyond her intelligence. She always knows which way to turn in a department store.

Come back to the calories. Once my doctor put me on a diet for medical reasons and it proved to be an illuminating experience. To begin with, various dishes at once appeared on our menu that we had not had for years, if ever before. They were dishes I had always liked since boyhood but which I had long since given up trying, by force or craft, to get served in my home because Nancy did not like them. They were among the foods that my doctor had excluded from my diet. I was under some strain watching Nancy eat them when I couldn't and I was hurt too, as hurt as she had ever been by my failure to understand. So I tried to find out why she was now serving hot breads, for instance, the biscuits, rolls and similar stuff that I had longed for in vain. The answer was simple: she had never known that I liked them. Since she did not like them and I had never mentioned them she had taken it for granted that my taste was the same as hers.

In such contexts a wife is always absolutely sincere. Nancy had never heard any of the demands or petitions I had made for hot biscuits through the years. But that simplicity got complicated at once, for she went on to explain that she had carefully avoided serving them to me, much as she had been tempted to. She had always known that they were bad for me and Dr. Smith's forbidding me to eat them now proved how right she had been. Pursuing the simplicities of male logic, I asked her why we were now having the prohibited dishes so often. I found out — in a way. "Why," Nancy said, "I simply decided there was no reason why I should go on denying myself forever since you couldn't eat them anyway."

That episode opens up a great deal of a wife's world. The key to it is my wife's surprise on learning for the first time that I liked kinds of foods I had been asking for through the whole course of our marriage. When to a wife's reproachful "Why didn't you tell me that? — you never tell me anything," a man answers, "You didn't listen," he is entirely wrong. The truth is simply that the line was busy when he phoned. The business of running a home is too important and too realistic for a woman to waste strength taking account of any such static fixture in it as a husband. Nancy read in a newspaper that I had been made an officer of a club. Why hadn't I ever told her I belonged to that club, she asked? I had never supposed that the information was necessary, since for years she had been having dinner with me there at short intervals. Turning a glance of sudden appraisal on me, she will say, "Why don't you ever wear blue shirts? I think you'd look good in blue." In a wife's world there will be no relation between that question and the fact that for years she has forbidden me to wear blue on the ground that she couldn't stand me in blue.

I am sure that that is why Nancy likes being married

to me: at any moment I may arrest her with the surprise of a wholly new revelation or discovery. "Why, I never knew you had an uncle in France!" she will say, and there is nothing a man could say in answer to such a remark even if he wanted to. Or, "Why didn't you ever tell me you were in the glee club in college?" — this, after years of acid comment on the songs I sing. Having always resolutely refused to let me gratify my ego by reading aloud — on the ground that she is not "ear-minded" and so cannot understand anything that is read to her — she will pause by the door when I am reading our youngest to sleep and later say, "It's too bad you don't like to read aloud, it would be nice if we did sometimes." And there is the periodically repeated, "Do you mean to say that you have concealed from me all these years . . ." well, that I went to school with a girl who is now a famous movie actress, that I am apprehensive about heights, or that a cousin of mine had six toes on one foot. Darling, I haven't been concealing it from you, I've been trying to tell it to you for nearly twenty years. But there is a filter in the communications system of a wife's world that screens out what a husband has to say.

That is why I say that Nancy has lived with a stranger all these years. She finds it exciting. The excitement, I hasten to say, is not the stranger but the sense of sin.

Or maybe there is another explanation. I have an uneasy feeling that she came close to revealing to me the status of husbands in the world wives live in one evening not long ago. We had spent the evening with some friends. When we got home I said that it seemed to me

Mary had been giving Joe something of a workout to-night, that she had been throwing her weight around quite a bit. She had talked, I said, as if she didn't have much respect for Joe's intelligence. Just how did she get that way? I wanted to know. Joe was a very bright guy indeed. Look what he'd done for himself — look where he stood in his profession — look at a large and miscellaneous bulk of evidence. Who the hell was Mary to snoot Joe's brains?

"Why, of course she doesn't respect his intelligence," Nancy said. I was glad that her observation had agreed with mine and I was preparing to go on with one of those candid character jobs on a friend that provide an endur-ing satisfaction of married life. Then a look that is hard to describe came into Nancy's eyes. It was speculative, it was amused, it was in a subtle way ribald and old as the earth and superior to the innocences and absurdities of men. "How could she?" Nancy went on, "She got him to marry her, didn't she?"

2

Virus Infection

LIKE YOU, I have just recovered from the annual epidemic. No one has been able to escape since the first cave man woke up with an impression that a mammoth had him by the throat. As always, I was moved to meditate on the triumphs of medical science and the mysterious psychology of wives. I don't know which is the more awe-inspiring, but medicine gets the better press.

Medicine won the victory with a phrase. I don't know what the cave man called his annual misery, but our grandfathers' name for it was "epizootic." Our parents preferred to speak of "la grippe" or, more often, "*the* la grippe." We grew up to call it "flu" or, with a touch of elegance, "influenza." All this troubled the stern, methodical men of science, for such names were inexact, and how can you make progress unless you are precise? Once the medical intelligence has been aroused, nothing can long hold out against it, and a few years ago the doctors announced that they had it at last: The plague was a Virus Infection. That was clearly that.

There have always been infallible remedies for this plague. At one time physicians opened a vein and took out a pint of the patient's blood. There was a period when they prescribed massive doses of calomel. Sweat baths had their glorious day, and so did the nonsolid diet, as well as complex combinations of vitamins, and electronic machines that produced heat deep in the body tissues. All these treatments were scientific to the last hairline on the scale, and all of them worked one hundred per cent. The patient took what the miracle worker prescribed, and hardly four or five days later the corrugations left his throat, the clamps stopped squeezing his muscles, the airplane motor that had been whirring inside his head fell silent, and he could begin to bore his friends with a long and explicit recital of medical details.

This year, when I decided there was no point in trying to kid myself — that the feeling of a windlass twisting the muscles of my arms and legs meant virus infection — I telephoned Joe, my old friend and family physician, and asked him what miracle medicine was now curing the plague. He said he would drop in and talk it over, which meant his wife had a committee meeting that evening and he wanted a couple of innings of backgammon.

When we settled down to play, he said virus infection was as universal and inescapable as the income tax — did I want him to take this up as a friend and scientist, or as a physician? As friend and scientist, he would recommend that I get an armful of mystery stories, go to bed, and resign myself with patience and good humor. (Here Nancy snickered offensively.) On the other hand, as a physician, he should employ the full resources of medicine for the patient's care. And, Joe said, medicine has a lot of resources.

He named a list of preparations with five hyphens and twenty-odd syllables apiece that were straight from the experimental clinics and had been altogether unknown a year before. All were infallible, all differed in some ways from the elixirs in green bottles the druggist kept in stock, and a few cost more than twice as much. Or, he said, he could really shoot the works and give me one of the true miracles of our day, the molds, the antibiotics. These are the sweethearts, Joe said — none of them will touch the virus beating that bass drum in your head, but any of them will cure you. None of them will make you feel much worse than the virus does — not for very long, any-way — and after they have cured you, you can recover from them in a week or ten days.

The plague had already progressed in me to the point where I found Joe's levity in bad taste. Seeing my ex-pression, he said there was simply no way out of feeling lousy for a few days; everybody had a virus infection and a birthday every year; he'd just got over it himself.

Here Nancy looked up from her book and asked aloofly what he'd done for it. I'll tell you what I did, Joe said. I went to the corner druggist and asked him what he recom-mended for virus infection. I took it, and it worked like a charm. Coming back to my problem, he said that, to tell the truth and lose money, the main thing was to do whatever would make me most comfortable — go to bed, and let Nancy take care of me. My wife closed her book and said briefly, Tomorrow is Wednesday.

An attack of virus infection is unavoidably bound up with the foundations of American family life, and it elicits from wives ideas and behavior that many people profess to find inexplicable. Well, they are mysterious on the surface, but they are not inexplicable. They are, in fact, logical to an extreme, though I confess it took me a long time to understand them. Here a man must not suppose that the theory of disease held by his wife is uniquely hers, for it is common to all wives.

The early stage of virus infection is paralleled by a stage in a wife's attitude toward it. Your muscles are merely tuning up their ache; the airplane motor is at half speed; you do not seriously think your temperature has climbed above 107 degrees; there is no sign of what Joe calls an upper respiratory infection. It isn't just a cold, I say to Nancy — if it were, my nose would be running. She tells me there is no need to be disgusting. I reply that colds do make noses run and that there can be no amazement in that fact for the mother of three children. Thereupon she exercises one of the most breath-taking talents wives have, that of numbing a husband's mind by pitching a third strike without a windup. When I get to feeling what a terrible mother I've been, she says, I can always remember that no child of mine ever had a cold. Though this may seem like dishonesty amounting to depravity, it is not. She believes what she has said purely, profoundly, and even passionately. It is part of the first stage of the attitude.

In this first stage, a wife is incredulous, disdainful of

masculine weakness, and rather bewildered. She accepts her husband's complaints as based on reality so far as to grant that perhaps he does feel some slight discomfort. But it is no worse than that which swallowing air with the formula causes an infant. Is the big ox (I am paraphrasing, for Nancy speaks fastidiously) going to make a fuss about *that?* She is puzzled, for this is the tough, dangerous guy who takes it for granted that his wife, and all women, think of him as a combination Arctic explorer, tennis champion and pugilist. He could take off his coat and play first base for the Giants any time, and no corner loafer had better give his wife the eye. Is this tireless, dominant male going to give up to a mere virus, something you can't even see? Well, honestly!

It is usually pleasant to look at Nancy, who is engagingly proportioned; but at such a moment her disgusting healthiness makes her look like a combination of lady wrestler and truck horse. Her insensitiveness to human suffering is exasperating to a man who feels as if he has just fallen out of a tenth-story window and landed on a ledge; but it is a mistake here (and for that matter at any other stage) to try to convince a wife that you do feel bad. Carelessly I say, Look, the very ends of my hair are sore. If you felt this way, you'd take to your bed instantly — but not before putting on your fetching nightgown with something frilly over it, and making up your lips so you'd look appealing when Joe got here. That illustrates a husband's tendency to lead with his chin. She nods and says, I thought so. You're frightened, aren't you? It isn't Joe you need, it's a psychiatrist.

She has arrived at the second stage. She has abandoned the idea that there is any physical cause here; her earlier notion was wrong. Now she understands that her husband honestly *thinks* he is sick, and she recognizes that this is serious. Concerned but patient, she says she supposes something unpleasant is scheduled at the office for tomorrow — he has to fire somebody, or there's a distasteful decision to be made — something like that. Sometimes we try to get out of things we don't want to do, she explains, by developing imaginary physical symptoms. (The sufferer decides that it is a mistake to teach women how to read and that books on popular psychology ought to be kept out of the lending libraries.) But you can't really get out of anything by feigning illness; eventually you have to face the unpleasantness, and it's better to face it than wait till your character has been undermined by subterfuge.

With dignity I explain that a regiment of dwarfs is pounding my muscles, my lungs and my skull with wooden mallets. Nancy represses her natural repugnance at what is both folly and weakness and explains that the whole point about imaginary ailments is that they *are* imaginary. A common mistake here is to try to prove your case — for instance, to get out a fever thermometer and use it. In the first place, people who are always taking their temperature are hypochondriacs, which is precisely what has just been pointed out to you. In the second place, when the thermometer records 101 degrees, that shows how dangerous hypochondria can be — see, you have actually frightened yourself into a temperature. You've got to start being stern with yourself right now. Why, if this were to go much farther, you could get sick.

One who did not know this woman would think her charming; but the plain truth is that she is a monster. She has no more feeling than a slab of granite; no more heart than a chunk of ice; and it becomes clear to the sufferer that his helpmeet is not only indifferent to his suffering, but actively hostile. He now understands why she brings home library books about the injustice of our prison system, why she believes criminals ought to be sent to sanitariums instead of to penitentiaries. She wants those penitentiaries reserved for people who really merit punishment — people who get sick. She regards him, he realizes with intensifying shock, as something much worse than a felon. A bank robber or a kidnaper is an unfortunate who cannot be held responsible. Such a person truly is sick and ought to be turned over to psychiatrists, who would cure him. But the real enemy of society — that is, of wives — is this creature who is uttering such unmanly moans about something less palpable than air.

And, besides, she knows he is committing this offense deliberately, of his own will and intent.

Do not dismiss this contention by saying that the sick man has worked up a grievance. There is grievance here, but it is the wife's; she has entered the third stage of the attitude. Now she holds that he has an invented, imaginary illness as well as a real illness, which he acquired purely out of malice. She has a feeling of intolerable affront, for he has entered on an ingenious plot against her.

Happily, this stage is short, for a wife's feeling of insult and a husband's feeling of injustice might lead to an exchange of unkind words.

The fourth stage comes when a wife faces the appalling fact that, whether this is an infantile pang in the stomach or is merely hypochondria, her husband is going to give in to it and is going to stay in bed. That is an inexpressible outrage; but she is a woman and therefore realistic; she will accept it and adjust to it. The world's work must be done. She must wash her hands of male fear and male malice and get about her business.

It now becomes clear that we have been looking at this whole episode from the wrong angle. The key to everything was Nancy's remark, Tomorrow is Wednesday. There is nothing mysterious in a wife's attitude toward illness if you remember that a wife is an Executive Vice-President in Charge of Plant and Production.

Nancy will observe the civilized amenities and bring a breakfast tray, though she would like to tell the malingering stranger in my bed that there are eggs and orange juice in the refrigerator if he's hungry. But what I resentfully interpret as repugnance in her manner is simply the preoccupation of the executive mind with its duties, which must now be discharged under an unusual handicap.

Already the stranger upstairs — there is no husband there after 8.30 A.M. — has thrown out of gear a delicately adjusted schedule, as sacred to the administrative officer of my family as the schedule of her opposite number at General Motors.

Trying to make me understand that I'm not sick, and

then making a special breakfast for me, made her late getting our youngest off to school. Being late with Tommy makes her late in planning the activities of the cleaning woman, who comes Wednesday, which makes her late in counting the laundry, and so on, with no hope of getting matters mended. You can't blame a virus for this destruction of efficiency; the oaf upstairs who thinks he is carrying the virus is to blame.

Late, and therefore with a wolf pack snapping at her heels, she comes upstairs. She makes her bed, but she can't make mine, for it has this repulsive and hypocritical object in it. Furthermore — at this hour of the morning! — an unknown man's clothes are scattered about. She hangs them in the closet or puts them in the hamper, with an expression on her face suggesting they may be radioactive.

She changes her clothes and makes up her lips — to even an ailing male she would be attractive if she weren't so revolting — and starts off. She says, remotely, You can't stay in this room. Ethel has to clean it. (It turns out that Ethel has to clean the children's rooms and every other room I settle down in. And if this were Thursday instead of Wednesday, there would be the man to repair the vacuum cleaner, or the paper hanger to make an estimate, or the program committee of the PTA.) She is off to her, to every wife's, fairest hour — at the shopping center.

When she returns, an intruder is wandering about the house. He is wearing the hideous and violently colored bathrobe her husband forcibly prevented her from giving to the Salvation Army, and the stubble on his face makes him look like a thug.

But the point, the intolerable point, is that he is in the way.

Eloise telephones to give her a summary of neighborhood news, and he is hanging over the banister to ask what in heaven's name she is giggling about. She has tackled the household accounts and has got halfway up a column of figures when he calls down that he can't find his camera and won't she have the charity to bring him a cup of coffee? She hangs out some woolens to air and, coming back, finds that, in a temporary renewal of hope, he has made himself a light lunch and the kitchen looks as if two trucks had collided there. She remembers with a sinking heart that she was going to go through the closets today, decides she can do it even if this cretin is on the loose, goes upstairs, and finds that he has spread his fishing tackle and gear all over the bedroom (with trout flies punched through the window curtains).

In short, her skepticism and apparent hostility on hearing about the symptoms of virus infection merely represented an Executive Vice-President's memory of what happened to the plant the last time a tornado struck it.

The basic law of an orderly universe, the foundation on which American life stands, is that any male who is in the house during working hours is the Enemy and must be regarded and treated as such.

About 5.20 P.M., Nancy comes upstairs, tranquilly humming something from the Hit Parade. She does her hair nicely and puts on a dress she knows I like, meanwhile chatting with me quite as if I belonged to the human race. She leaves a print of her lips in crimson on a square of tissue and says gently, Poor angel, you've felt miserable, haven't you? She draws me out about the manifold discomforts that I have endured so unprotestingly.

There follows a period of agreeable conversation, and I perceive that this is indeed a warmhearted and sympathetic woman.

She says suddenly, You'd like a cocktail, wouldn't you? She goes out and presently returns with a tray, a couple of glasses and a shaker. She says, Of course I can never make them with the finesse you do. This may be one of the crudest ways of inflating the male ego, but it is also the straightest and surest way to any man's admiration.

So she sits down on her bed, and we sip our cocktails, and a fine sense of accord and mutual satisfaction settles on us. I feel distinctly better, and that certainly is a nice dress, and this is a pleasant place, and my wife has a very attractive smile.

Nancy smiles now, reminiscently and charitably, and there is regret for my suffering in that smile, and scorn for the unpredictable hazards of this world. You were lucky to have such a short siege of it, she says. Why, just think, you'll be able to go to the office tomorrow.

3

The Monster in the Home

EVERY so often, from an abyss of self-abasement, Nancy says to me, "Do you suppose we really are as dreadful as They think we are?" There isn't a parent in the world who doesn't know that "They" are our children. The answer to Nancy's question is: Darling, we're a darned sight too good for them, and I'm for taking a stand. I have no desire to abolish The War Between Children and Parents. It is every child's right, and a necessary part of the process that will eventually make him a human being, to consider his parents not only more cruel and tyrannical than the warden of the debtors' prison in a Dickens novel, but feeble-minded, obsolete and socially deplorable. I'm strong for letting them exercise the right; but I say the counterattack is long past due. We are, I repeat, too good for the little monsters, and I'm for the Parents' Revolution. The trouble is, we have let them take the offensive, and we are now in full retreat. We have to stop letting them get away with it; we have to win back some sizable part of the United States and make it safe for parents. Association with our children is robbing us of our self-esteem. But what is worse, it is weakening our intelligence, corrupting our manners and undermining our morals.

It is a commonplace that Donnie's parents are far more interesting than we are, that Billy's have a decent modicum of wealth, which enables them to furnish their house in a manner worthy of their children, that Susy's are devoted to thinking up nice things to give her, that, in fact, everybody else's parents exceed the minimum standards of which the parents of our children fall short.

I know, Nancy said. When I catch Caroline looking at me with a pity that has triumphed over her shock, or the inflection she can get into the word "Mother," which reveals an overstrained but still generous tolerance for a cretin — Caroline is fifteen years, one month, and two days old as of this morning. She calls me "Pops," a patronizing monosyllable that her brother Dick, nearly two years older, brought into our family life as the tolerance of maturity broadened his sympathies. It is true that she frequently is patient with Nancy, and this shows she has a generous heart. But, I said, that is precisely my point. Generosity, patience, kindness toward the unfortunate and the crippled are sterling virtues, but look who's exercising them on us. And my further point is that Caroline is steadily debasing us.

For instance, I said to Nancy, a couple of days ago I heard you refer to one of our acquaintances as a "bristle-beaned square," and I have observed a number of such expressions creeping into your speech. They spoke English in your family and at your school and college, and you have a pleasing, if perhaps too readily exercised, gift for expressing yourself. It will wither away, for nobody can stand daily exposure to the gibberish that is our daughter's medium of communication without catching something like verbal typhoid. I would not object if the gibberish had any of the vigor, poetry, or healthy vulgarity of slang, but it hasn't. It is a blubberlike patter that any of the lower apes could master, but an imbecile would find insufficient for his needs. But our prima donna has it figured out that we are the imbeciles in this cast. I want to know why.

I can take it, Nancy said — I understand what she says a good part of the time, and I don't mind being dealt with as an antique in matters of behavior and social correctness, or as a mental defective whose fumbling ideas have to be explained to the younger set. You're right in calling that sort of thing a normal part of the War of the Generations, and we asked for it when we volunteered to become parents. But I will admit I get a touch worn down by our darling's prudery and puritanism on behalf of the elderly. It's all right for you to have a cocktail — poor old Pops is entitled to the consolations of senility. But if I take one with you, I am heading straight toward alcoholism, and we'd better draw the curtains to keep the neighbors from seeing my shame. It's indecent for a woman of my age to use lipstick. I haven't a single dress she approves of, and do you know what's wrong with them? They're all immoral.

Nancy was telling the truth. My daughter is shocked by any evidence that anyone finds Nancy attractive. Caroline can understand that a male eye as old as mine may occasionally kindle at Mother, who is forty, because old men are disgusting. It says so in some book her set has read. But sometimes a man who is only in late middle age, crowding thirty, will exhibit approval of Mother, and that *is* Nancy's fault. Mother is wearing a dress proper only to the high school set, and she is flaunting herself with dissolute shamelessness.

What I call to your attention, I said to Nancy, is the source from which this fastidious criticism comes. I've known you, I went on, since your teeth were in braces, and there was never a time when you would not have rejected Caroline's usual costume as unfit to wear if you were sweeping out the coal cellar. The shirt she has been wearing for six weeks is one Dick threw away. I cannot call Dick a finicky dresser, but at least he tucked the tail inside his dungarees — which Caroline calls "unhappy slacks." The shirttail floats over the patch on the rear of her dungarees with all the charm of a dish towel hanging on a line. Your shoes may be immoral, but what does she wear? Either her tennis sneakers of summer before last or a pair of saddle shoes she has brought within the sanction of fashion by wading in a swamp with them on.

It is this battered rose, I said, whom your gaucherie and crassness offend. But the repulsive appearance of adolescents bothers me less than the fear that they may drag parents down to their standards, especially their moral standards. Nancy looked startled. Why, Caroline is as innocent as a baby, she said, and at fifteen she is as sexless as a glass of water. That is true, but I reminded my wife that there are other kinds of morals. The garment Caroline put on over her brother's shirt this morning, I said, may look like a saddle blanket, but it is a boy's pea jacket, though Caroline calls it a "vegetable coat." It belonged to the one she calls Sloopy, and if you cannot distinguish Sloopy among the queer life-forms that troop through this house, he is the one who makes noises like a whooping crane. She decided that she wanted it, so she took it, and she will not give it back. The sounds of a whooping crane in agony issue from our telephone for ninety minutes at a stretch, but Caroline goes on wearing Sloopy's vegetable coat. That, I pointed out, was called stealing in the antique morality from which our children have been so happily emancipated. Her moral position is further weakened by the fact that, in her judgment, Sloopy is by no means a dream-beam; he is, in fact, a square, a creep, and a drip strictly from the faucet. Now, see where that brings her out. She is brighter than Sloopy — not an immoderate testimonial to her intelligence — so she is exploiting human weakness, which is immoral. Besides that, she is trading on what we must agree to call her feminine charm, in order to defraud a boy she dislikes of his haberdashery, and his coke money, and the use of the family automobile. That makes her a moral leper, and what will happen to us if we go on associating with her?

A troubled expression appeared on Nancy's face. It occurred to me, I went on, that our unjustified affection for our children deludes us into misunderstanding their true nature. They are certainly superior to us in one respect — they understand each other much better than we understand them. And how? By the exercise of what to our gentler minds seems a repulsive cynicism but in fact is only realism. They habitually attribute the lowest possible motives to each other, and in the end it invariably turns out that they were right.

Our children's cynicism is the greatest stabilizing force in our family life, because it provides a reciprocal discipline. Or perhaps I should say a drawn battle. Dick's two years' advantage in age exactly compensates for Caroline's greater versatility in malice, bad sportsmanship and dishonorable methods of warfare. Their mutual wariness and distrust maintain a kind of armed truce and speedily restore it when it has been broken. If Dick finds that a couple of dollar bills are missing from under the loosened floor board in his clothes closet, he need lose no time in identifying the thief. He knows who she is, and he knows the most effective reprisal and the exact amount of it that will be permitted him. He is an eloquent storyteller, given to narratives about his school's athletic hero, intellectual giant and dream-beam of all girls, the Hewes boy, known to worshipful myriads as "Dick." Any parental disposition to be impressed is neutralized by Caroline, who is in possession of the facts, or, if not, assumes as a matter of course that he is lying and rushes to discharge her duty of proclaiming the truth.

On the other hand, in our home there are few tragic dramas of a girl wounded by someone's callous disregard, crushed by the world's sorrow or regally repudiating the gross misconceptions of her fineness held by the ignoble. Many such scenes get under way; but Dick saw Olivia de Havilland in that one, or he picks up the speech and finishes it from one of last night's radio programs. Each of our adolescents carries a club, brass knuckles and a knife; the knowledge each has of the other's armament makes for peace. Well, that may not quite be the word.

My attire does not arouse shame in Dick, as Nancy's does in Caroline. It merely mortifies him. He feels that flashiness and informality are unbecoming my age, and when they are manifested by my neckwear, he takes curative measures. What he does with my ties I cannot say, for I have not known him to wear a necktie since he was twelve, except to dances, and then only such as he would never find on my rack or anywhere else short of a fireworks factory. He feels that at my age one should wear only black ties and, for that matter, should dress all in black, except for the shirt, which may be plain white. He is forced to admonish me about my behavior, too, in private hardly less often than in public. From a sensitive feeling for propriety, he instructs me when to lower my voice. And it seems I have ways of standing and sitting that must be corrected, physical and verbal awkwardnesses that make me more than a little conspicuous.

This concern about my clothes comes from a beau of fashion whose shirt is a sports model with six-inch diamond-shaped figures in purple and green printed on the background of a stormy sunset. He alternates this with a modish number in flannel; bright red, with C.H.S. on the front and the numeral 4 on the back — this is alleged to have been worn by a predecessor of his on the baseball team, who attained the big leagues but must have retired a generation ago. The voice in which he admonishes me to lower mine has a carrying power of three miles and when raised in the streets at night, wakes lonely spinsters to terror. My unseemly posture usually stimulates him to reproof when he is trying to fulfill a lifelong ambition to sit in a chair so that the back of his neck touches the seat.

Dick is a kindly and helpful youth, ever willing to correct the mistakes of his parents. They are manifold, continuous and of long standing; but probably they are most evident in our management of our children. True, when he scrutinizes himself, he finds evidence that we did not err much with our firstborn — that is, till recently. Perhaps, indeed, our only serious mistakes with him have been financial; our parsimony has prevented him from living according to his station and has handicapped him in the use of his many talents for civilized pleasure. But this defect can be repaired at any time; there is nothing that cannot be righted by larger subsidies and, say, an automobile.

After a promising start as parents, we went to pieces. Caroline's birth plunged us into benighted stupidity. Dick grants that the problems she faced us with were dismaying, but he cannot pardon our softness or our blindness to its results. He would come close to finding Caroline not responsible for the mess she has become, since our indulgence, favoritism and craven unwillingness to face the facts are where the real blame lies. He must dissociate himself from the failure we have made with her, since day by day he has clearly pointed out to us wherein we were wrong. We have always let her get away with murder; worst of all, we have abetted her in her most constant atrocity, which is her disregard of his rights, prerogatives and dignities. From the beginning, we should have taught her to be respectful, to be quiet and unobtrusive, to conduct herself in decorous and seemly ways, to appreciate the qualities of those a couple of years older than herself, and most of all to keep her trap shut.

Having seen us fail ignominiously with Caroline, Dick was prepared for what has happened with his younger brother. He has always freely advised us about Tommy, and in the past year his counsel has been seasoned with insight picked up in his psychology course. Our home life has been enriched by such terms as "antisocial," "Oedipean involvement," "infantile drive" and "primitive impulse from the unconscious." He puts enlightenment at our disposal, though with only the barest hope that we may be qualified to profit from it. To hope at all shows his courage, after what happened with Caroline, and with a detachment proper to the critical mind, he sees that in Tommy also we have produced a noisome brat. The antipodes meet here, and, uniquely, Caroline sees eye to eye with Dick, and like him ascribes the appalling result to our favoritism and stupidity. We are able to see only that the pair has developed in Tommy a realism more formidable than their own. He has survived by fitness; he has acquired guile, craft and cunning so superior to theirs that he manages both of them with a sure touch, setting one against the other and thus living comfortably in a situation that otherwise would daily threaten him with destruction. He has learned how to take monsters in his stride and bend them to his purposes and profit. I look forward with confidence to his adolescence; he will achieve triumphs of offensiveness far beyond their powers.

Something is to be said for Dick's man-of-the-world urbanity, the tolerance long acquaintance with the dullness of his elders has given him, as against Caroline's vociferous outrage. Caroline sets us right primarily from self-interest, to prevent us from disgracing her among the younger set; but Dick feels what can only be called *noblesse oblige*. The well-informed are under obligation to instruct the ignorant; the sagacious must do what they can to keep the foolish from folly; and those gifted at logic must point out errors in reasoning. The frequency of our errors does not discourage him; sometimes curtly, sometimes wearily, but usually affably, and always instantaneously, he pursues them to their source, sets things right, and gives us a new start. True, the Plight of Modern Youth, of which his school has informed him, is our personal fault. Between us we brought on the war that destroyed Youth's Heritage, created Race and Class Conflict, filled the slums with the Delinquent Child, made the Future so black that only his dauntless generation could do anything about it, and passed the statute that forbids him to drive my car as fast as he would like. Our personal responsibility must be pointed out to us, and is, most eloquently just when he has been told to mow the lawn or shovel some of the debris from his room.

But, I said to Nancy, a great day will come. Parents of the world will unite, knowing they have nothing to lose but their pains, and the church bells will ring in a new era. The revolution will begin by proclaiming the great truth that, though our children may be fit to associate with their own subhuman kind, they are not fit to associate with savages, still less with us. I do not know why we do the savages the bitter injustice of comparing our offspring with them, for savages are tolerant, they bathe sometimes, and they would change their socks if they had socks.

I frequently find myself wondering, I said, just what will touch off the revolution. There will be a last drop of water that finally shatters the stone, a single snowflake more that starts the avalanche. I think I know when that will happen. There will come a moment when Dick raises his head from his book to help my befuddled mind deal with Congress, say, or with my job. The last snowflake will fall when I point out that what he is reading is a comic book — and one that he stole from Tommy's room. That, I will suggest, makes him an authority only on comic books.

I know what my snowflake is going to be, Nancy said. Once too often Caroline will spread some mayonnaise on her chocolate cake. I have moments of wondering whether it isn't a nightmare — sandwiches of fudge and liverwurst, candy bars spread with anchovy paste, dill pickles with cherry pie — but it isn't a nightmare; that's what she likes to eat. She can't, I will tell her sometime, recognize good taste in any form.

I have found a vivid word in the dictionary, I said

— "filicide," which means murdering one's children. No doubt society is right in making filicide a crime, though perhaps the penalty placed on it is too severe. I couldn't find any word that means the wish to commit filicide, but that wish is so common and so consoling that there must be a name for it. You and I need that word, the multitude of oppressed and inferior parents need it; but I can't find it. Well, Nancy said, you can always ask Dick.

4

Topic One

WHEN the generals and admirals hold war games, everybody has a good time and nobody gets shot. A similar way of fighting the War Between Men and Women provides one of the most durable pleasures of marriage. The game is played like chess, for the satisfaction of outthinking one's opponent, or like tennis, for the satisfaction of a good workout and an amicable discussion of the match over a cool drink later on. There are no victories, for one player uses male logic and the other female logic, which never meet at any point. Checkmate would be impossible if one player's pieces were checkers and the other's dominoes. At tennis the score would always be love-all or deuce if one player were hitting the ball with a golf club and the other with a billiard cue. Perhaps love-all is the better count here.

Nancy brought home from a tea party a new variation of the desert-island question. As everyone knows, the usual form of the question is: If you had to spend the rest of your life on a desert island with just one companion and were free to choose anyone, whom would you pick? I interrupted Nancy before she could quote the new variation. I reminded her that some years ago a movie actress closed the discussion forever. When she got back from Europe, the massed reporters of New York found nothing better to ask her than the old cliché. With what, I now told Nancy, was admirably clear thinking, the girl said, "I'd choose a good obstetrician."

Nancy expresses both amusement and disdain by wrinkling her nose. It was practically corrugated now as she alluded to the coarseness of my mind. The question she had been asked, she said, was extremely serious. The problems it posed were so difficult that you had to disregard what the movie girl was thinking about — you had to leave All That out. Moreover, the terms of the question were that you could not choose the person you were married to. Even, Nancy said, even in the unlikely contingency that a woman would want to.

The tea had been given for a visiting English novelist, a woman. She seemed to find the literary conversation oppressive. Observing that Nancy did not take to it either, the novelist engaged her in a cozy chat about children, salads, where to buy hats and other subjects that led straight to women's exasperation with men. A glow of understanding and accord warmed them both. It was in this mood of fellowship that the novelist asked thoughtfully, If you had to spend the rest of your life on a desert island with just one companion, would you choose a man or a woman?

Nancy boasts that she has no interest in hypothetical questions. She says that only the illogical male sex wastes time on things that don't exist or can't happen. But this question so fascinated and even disturbed her that she had felt obliged to think it through. It made you weigh everything you had learned from experience. You had to decide what your basic values were, and what life in those solemn circumstances called for. So she had done some strenuous thinking and had come to a conclusion. She did not want me to feel hurt — I must not take her conclusion personally. I must remember that the question was hypothetical, that actually she wasn't going to spend the rest of her life on a desert island. But if she were going to, logic and realism would permit only one answer. She would be forced to choose a woman.

I said, You certainly are disregarding All That, but I don't know if you can. One morning you and your chosen companion stroll over to the other side of the island and find Friday's footprint in the sand, large and unmistakably male — what happens then? Nancy said I was making my usual ridiculous assumption about women, and besides, the question meant what it said — one other person on the island, not two. She was as surprised as I could be by her conclusion, she said, but the reasons that had forced it on her were interesting. There were a lot of them. But, Nancy said, the fundamental reason is that women are usually gentlemen and men usually aren't, and if you had to spend the rest of your life confined on an island with a person who wasn't a gentleman, it would be plain hell.

I could not, I told her, have been more surprised if she had asserted that women usually have three legs.

Women, I said, were not created to be gentlemen, and their charm largely comes from their repudiating the whole concept of being gentlemen. Nancy said that this universal belief of men was one of the absurdities of the male ego. All the ideas men have about themselves are unrealistic, she said, but the oddest one is this notion that they behave like gentlemen. Of course, Nancy observed with firm finality, when the going gets rough, only women do.

It happens that last summer Dick distinguished himself by reaching the finals in a tennis tournament. He came close to winning the cup, but he lost it. In what looked as if it would be the last game of the match, the umpire called a point in Dick's favor which Dick thought he had actually lost. So, naturally, on the next point he drove the ball out of the court, and the other boy came back to take the game and eventually the match. Nancy cried a little and was warmly maternal to Dick. But when she expressed herself to me in private, she was furious: clearly Dick was the better player; he'd had the match all but won, and then he had thrown it away because of an idiotic convention!

I now reminded her of that judgment, and she promptly went into battle formation. Oh, *games!* she said. There would be no games on this manless island. Games were just a way in which the male ego found expression, and women would never play them if left to themselves. Games are men showing off male strength and skill, she said, so that women will be impressed, you dearly hope. As for this idea that you must not take advantage of an umpire's error or an opponent's tough luck, it's just silly. Men made it up so that the male ego could admire men as dead-game sports. If women ran things, you'd play tennis by the rules, and if your opponent fell down or the umpire handed you a point, so much the better. Honestly, does it make sense to play a game and not play it to win? If you're playing for that cup, do you want it or not? But of course, Nancy said, men aren't realistic.

I pointed out that feminine realism was taking a fall out of feminine chivalrousness, and she couldn't have it both ways. I added that woman's endeavor was to have it both ways and, getting back to being a gentleman, had she ever seen women at a bargain sale? When a department store advertises a sale of blouses, I went on, it protects the neighboring counters with sandbags. The police rope off the arena and detail a dozen traffic cops and two platoons of patrolmen to confine the carnage to the devastated area. Hordes of you gentlemen converge on the place, and two hours later the emergency wards are full. In the games the male ego makes rules for, biting in the clinches is prohibited. A player who slugs another one gets sent off the field, and heaven knows what would happen if he pulled an opponent's pants off. I've seen you, I told her, come back from one of those riots with your ribs bruised, your shins raw, your skirt ripped and your hair needing a new wave.

A smile curved Nancy's lips, and she said she was glad to have me make her points for her. I had described the purest realism, she said. A woman at a sale hewed to the line, disregarding everything that didn't bear on her purpose. She went to a sale to save money, and nothing could be more realistic than that. You may save a dollar thirty-one on the blouse, I said, but you pay four dollars to taxi into town and back. It was her eyebrows that wrinkled now, and she said, It would be poor economy for you if I took a bus; why, I wouldn't be fit to live with when I got home. I'd be tired out and shrewish.

I saw a hole between tackle and guard and prepared to send the tailback through it by remarking, You wouldn't act like a gentleman, you mean? But she blocked the play. She said I talked so irrelevantly because men did not go to bargain sales. Did I remember the time I took her to an Army-Notre Dame football game? On that purely male occasion, seventy-five thousand people had tried to storm those little gates. If there had been a gentleman in the crowd, he would have been trampled to death. She would concede, however, that trampling would be an appropriate end for anyone silly enough to submit to the violence of that mob and the cold gale of that day in order to look at a game. It isn't realistic, she said, and a bargain sale is. When I go to one, it's to buy a blouse — and I buy a blouse. Nothing stops me. As you sportsmen say, I bring home the bacon.

I said that we had got a long way from the desert island and that what had taken us on the detour was Topic One. For it is a mistaken notion, I said, that sex, or All That, is the commonest subject of conversation between or within the sexes. Nancy said swiftly, With men Topic One is How Well I Understand Women. I pronounced that with women Topic One is Women Are the Realistic Sex. And,

I said, that is women's most charming delusion. Realistic?
— say paradoxical, shifty, tricky, fast on their feet, quick
thinking, anything that will suggest the cunning and guile
of your sex, but never realistic. Like logic, I said, realism
is a sex-linked character, and the sex it's linked to is the
male.

Nancy said joyfully, All right, I'll prove it. Men and
the male grouse! Take men of your age. (Clearly the
late eighties, she seemed to be thinking.) They spend
three-quarters of an hour shaving and applying what they
lack the realism to call cosmetics, and being enchanted by
what the mirror shows them. Then they put on that beautiful brown suit — you ought never to wear brown, of
course, but you won't listen to what I say — and an off-
white shirt and that expensive tie and your Homburg.

Wait a minute, I said, Never in my life have I worn a
Homburg. Why is it, Nancy said, that men always apply
a generalization personally? I'm talking about men of
your age. So you swagger down the sidewalk, certain that
every woman feels her pulse leap and sees how life has
let her down. The poor old simpleton has got himself all
prettied up for the yearning female glance — and women
never look at him. Wait, Nancy said, I'm talking. Well,
when a woman gets dressed to the nines, has any of that
hard work been done with men in mind? Not a bit of it.
She was aiming at the female glance. And she had better
know her stuff, for believe me, it is going to be leveled at
her in the spirit of critical appraisal. That, Nancy said,
closing the subject, that's realism. Does a woman waste
effort dressing to make men look at her? She knows

darned well nothing can keep them from looking at her.

I said she was going to find life on the desert island pretty dull, with no male intelligence to feel superior to. No, not dull, she said, it's going to be so *restful*. Just think, a fuse blows out or a door comes off the hinges, and now it's just a matter of putting in a new fuse or screwing the hinge back. We won't have to swoon with admiration of the male cleverness that is able to replace a fuse. Honestly! the time women spend saying how wonderful a man is because, with only a basement workshop and three hundred dollars' worth of tools, he has learned how to mend the toaster! He brings that toaster upstairs, and he's beating his chest as if he had killed a mammoth and dragged it to the cave for his mate and her young. The job a woman never gets time off from is appreciating that her man has just killed a mammoth. Even when he's only been daring enough to tell a waiter that this isn't the kind of salad his mate ordered.

Her chest-beating mate, Nancy continued, is the undisputed champion of this valley. He is a very dangerous guy, you bet. His woman has got to know that at any moment she may have to throw herself between him and some unfortunate who has roused his anger. She has got to restrain him, for he doesn't realize his own strength, and what a glorious providence it was, now wasn't it? that sent her a mate who is one-hundred-and-fourteen-per-cent male. Even golf — if his chip shot makes the green, she has got to feel as if he has flung her face down across his horse and galloped away with her. And I've never understood, Nancy said, why it's such a tremendous feat for this muscle-bound Hercules to haul in a fish. There it is in a nutshell: On our island we'll catch fish because we want something to eat, not to keep an ego shored up.

I said she was still trying to have it both ways. The male ego could be as overpowering as she said or it could be as frail as she said, but it couldn't be both, and how did she want to play it? But I was about ready to throw in my hand, I said; she had me pretty well convinced. Still, I would like to know what this novelist looked like. Nancy giggled. Like any prominent Englishwoman, she said, like a horse that someone has thrown a bolt of tweed at. I said that the mutual courtesy of women was matched only by their mutual candor. Nonsense, Nancy said, I've heard you say that the Englishman's love of horses is founded solidly on the looks of Englishwomen, and anyone can see that the English girdle industry could use American know-how.

I said I couldn't find any flaw in her reasoning, yet I foresaw trouble at Desert Acres. For instance, I said, with no male ego on this island, you are going to be denied most common topics of conversation. There isn't much left for you two realists to be realistic about except each other. In time the clothes you and Aggie, or whatever her name is, were shipwrecked in will wear out. To prepare for the candid female gaze, you've got only a common stock of grasses and palm leaves. It looks to me like a perpetually tied game. So one day you try on the two-piece creation that you have been plaiting for a month, and standing by the pier glass, you ask Aggie what she thinks of it. Aggie tells you. She says, Not with your hips, dear.

You keep telling me I haven't got any hips, Nancy said, and you claim that what I've got in place of hips is extremely attractive.

Attractive, charming, eye-filling, I said, but I'm an unrealistic male — and besides, you're bragging, you're beating your chest because you've mended the toaster, which is too masculine a trait for Desert Acres. The realistic Aggie will have no concern about any pleasant lines to the southwest you may possess — her restful intelligence is going to be focused on laying up plenty of mammoth. Any beauty shop sorcery you may practice will simply make her remark that there isn't going to be any ship, my girl, and we're entirely out of firewood. I also hear Aggie's grunt when you tell her to run upstairs and get your brown handbag or when you remember that you didn't put the car away.

I understand the restfulness of having no male ego to build up, I said, but I still say disaster is on the way. There comes a moment when one of you just happens to get reminiscent about one of the abandoned topics. I wonder what the other realist will make of your memories of those unrestful days before the shipwreck: the scores of forlornly fascinated men; the women whose reason for disliking you was perfectly plain; your pass defense; in a word, your record. Aggie has a woman's courteous candor for a woman's conviction that when she takes off down the sidewalk, every male eye fastens on her and gleams.

You know very well, Nancy said, you're delighted when men stare at me with a gleam in their eyes. Certainly, it's a tonic to my ego, I said, but I won't be on this island paradise, and there won't be any male eyes, either. Aggie is going to say, Dear, could you have been wrong about that gleam? Conversation at Desert Acres is going to be based on the strictest female realism, just like the restful daily chores that will be straight to the point. So far as Aggie is concerned, those remembered gleams are an illusion of your ego.

It is going to be quite different on my island, I went on. My thinking comes out just where yours does, and I'm forced to make the same choice. If I must spend my life on a desert island with just one companion, I choose a woman, too. Nancy snorted. Every man gets the desert-island fantasy at a certain age, she said, and for some mysterious reason it's always a blonde. Too bad the blonde skin toughens to rawhide in the sun and the blonde hair fades to the color of old rope. You're thinking of her as straight from the chorus line and bursting out of her clothes in the right places, but in six months she'll look like a Stone Age squaw.

No, I said, for she's a realist. In the frantic moments before abandoning ship, while you and Aggie were collecting axes and bean pots and stout denim coveralls, this girl (Girl! Nancy murmured) was otherwise engaged. She was gathering make-up materials and the kind of clothes it would be pleasant to see her burst out of.   At the end of the day, when I drag up the carcass of a mammoth, the restfulness of our cave will be based on a hostess gown and the adept use of lipstick and a good eye shadow.

How perfectly male! Nancy said. And, excuse me, how disgustingly senile of you. Can't you see that this is a serious question? You're supposed to decide what counts most, which means you have to use your mind. I guess you did, at that, she conceded, but you ought to scrub your mind with a strong phenol solution before using it.

I'm being realistic, as you most certainly aren't, I said. Lipstick and eye shadow represent a very feminine impulse. And since I may have to spend a long time on this island, I want it well stocked with feminine impulses.

I perceived that beginning right now I was going to have to watch the clock on the scoreboard very closely. I might have known, Nancy said, that you would take a generalization as some kind of attack on you. You're mad, aren't you? You're perfectly furious. Even so, it's pretty low to call me unfeminine.

Nothing could be farther from my mind than to call you that, I said. I was speaking hypothetically.

When a man says he's speaking hypothetically, Nancy said, you can be dead sure he's talking about his wife. Just name one way I'm unfeminine!

I decided I could risk one more point before driving the ball out of the court. Always speaking hypothetically, I said, I point out that it's unfeminine to be masculine.

Me masculine? Nancy gasped. Why —

I'm told, I said, that an ego which requires constant building up by its mate is masculine. The deepening color in Nancy's cheeks was the hands of the clock reaching zero. So, tightening my grip on my racket, I said, You leaped to an unwarranted conclusion about my companion's coloring. She isn't a blonde, she's an identical twin.

Now it's bigamy! Nancy said, with a glitter rather than a gleam in her eye.

I said a twin, not twins, I pointed out. I must believe, I hurried on, that you were led into error by your instincts as a gentleman. Otherwise, you would see that you would always be under false pretenses on this island. You have accepted the reasoning of a shapeless bolt of tweed and an unavailing girdle. I assume, too, I added, that the lipstick was purple and there was no eye shadow.

Some orange rouge on the cheekbones, Nancy said, but you can't make up horses, anyway.

Precisely, I said. The choice of a woman companion was realistic, but it was the realism of necessity. I'm dead sure that your twin would not be misled by what it is kind to regard as misfortune.

Will you, Nancy demanded, tell me what all this talk about twins means? I haven't got a twin.

I am forced to create a sister for you, I said. The terms stated were that one could not choose the person he was married to. A realist who has been married to my wife would not even consider the hypothesis unless he could choose her twin.

Nancy said, Oh.

I watched the ball soar over the backstop, and a rosy pink replace the red that had come to her cheeks. Presently she said, They actually served tea — aren't you going to make a cocktail? As I rose to do so, she added reflectively, I suppose the question doesn't make sense. You couldn't realistically leave All That out, could you?

I choose Nancy. And, it is clear, I'd better.

5

The Impatient Patient

NANCY said she guessed she had caught the bug, all right, and that it would be sensible to spend a couple of days in bed. She added, You'll simply have to cope, poor lamb. There was in her voice a suggestion of a four-star general, on the eve of D-Day, saying, Well, Hewes, I'm sorry. You'll have to take over. Then she made preparations for a thoroughly delightful time.

We are right to feel sorry for a woman who has caught the influenza virus, for she suffers intensely. The astonishing trouble we get into results from the fact that we sympathize with her for the wrong reasons; we mistake the nature of her suffering. I maintain that this woman can be understood. But we do need a new theory. I am not sure whether it is a new theory of medicine or of magic.

Nancy's vision of spending a couple of days in bed means release. Somebody else can attend to the require-

ments of the household, or they can go hang. She is going to sleep as late as she wants to, till noon anyway, and
that hasn't happened since her first baby. She is going to
recline on two or three extra pillows and catch up by telephone with all her friends. She is going to read mystery
stories and paint her toenails a bright red and do nothing
whatever. Besides, a woman sometimes wants to be
waited on and coddled and spoiled a little. It's only
human to want some extra attention occasionally.

Her idea of idleness and luxury is just fantasy. The unfortunate wench is licked before she starts. Emotions that
will shatter the vision to bits are already fermenting in
her. She doesn't know that yet, but we must know it in
order to understand her.

For one thing, there is what happens to a man between
9 A.M. and 5 P.M., especially if, like Nancy's husband, his
profession permits him to do much of his work at home.
A woman may remember that the person with whom she
shares her life is lovable and even in some ways bright;
but between those hours he is transformed into an enemy
dangerously loose in her house. Again, just below her
consciousness, there is a feeling of affront. She is a mem-
ber of the tough sex; illness is for men, who are fragile
and delicately organized and neurotic. It is not logical
for this virus to attack her, and a moment will arrive
when she can take no more irrationality and will require
the world to behave logically. Finally, the manager of the
home is the last universal specialist surviving in society,
the master of all trades, the Expert. So long as she stays
in bed, the watchman has forsaken his crossing, the engi-

neer his switchboard, the pilot his controls. These psychological jigsaw parts are certain to come together with some violence of one kind or another.

Nancy woke at her usual 6.45, of course; a woman with children in school does. She had a fine feeling of contentment, lying in bed through the breakfast hour, but she was sure that Dick would take advantage of the situation by omitting to change his shirt; whereas Caroline would put on the green sweater she has been ordered not to wear to school, now that she is beginning to fill out. Tommy would breakfast on what was left of the chocolate cake, and I could be expected to gash my fingers at the unfamiliar task of opening a can of orange juice. Also, the house was filled with the smell (entirely imaginary) of burning toast. Yet such pinpricks were compensated for by the novelty of having the morning paper all to herself and leisure to read her way through every department store ad.

It did seem an odd time for someone to be driving a herd of cattle through the downstairs. (It is an open question whether from now on noise or silence in the house is more disturbing.) Presently she initiated the day's upstairs-downstairs dialogue by asking how much of the front porch Dick had taken with him when he left. I replied that there was no unusual noise, that this was just the normal and orderly departure of our children for school; only, not being in the middle of it, she was not half deafened. Understand, a husband tells these lies protectively, to spare the invalid's feelings. Also, I was unwilling to admit that our children's father could not keep down their decibel-production as effectively as their mother does.

Nancy was pleased when I took up the orange juice that was all she wanted for breakfast. True, I had put one of her linen napkins on the tray, though the pantry was full of paper ones, and had added a blossom from her azalea, thus doubtless ruining the plant; but she allowed for the nine-to-five stupidity of males. On my part, I observed that she had tidied up the bedroom, done her hair most attractively, applied lipstick several shades brighter than she usually wears, and put on a fresh nightgown with trailing sleeves and over it a pink thing with a flirtatious collar and a lot of bows — called, I believe, a bed jacket. I had been thinking of her as haggard with pain, but she looked like a highly paid model who had consented to a screen test.

I remarked that I saw she had summoned Joe and that the measure seemed a little extreme, considering that she had been unable to push the thermometer quite to a hundred degrees. Nancy said, Certainly I phoned Joe. If I'm going to be sick, I might as well enjoy it. Why, if you had a temperature of a hundred, you'd be yelling for Joe to bring an ambulance to get you to the hospital in time.

The doctor's visit is the last part of a woman's illness that lives up to her fantasy. For three-quarters of an hour, while I attended to household tasks, bursts of soprano and baritone laughter echoed down to me. When Joe came down, refreshed by this restful interlude, he said that there was no point in doing anything about influenza except to stay in bed — just make sure that Nancy did so. I expressed a hope that none of his danger-list cases had perished while he was catching up with the neighborhood gossip at my expense.

Upstairs, Nancy was finding out that she had selected a singularly dull lot of mystery stories. This marks a stage in the fading of the vision; though still disguised, the pressures are rising. They intensify as the doorbell, the telephone and the upstairs-downstairs dialogue sharpen the conflict between male ignorance and the household manager's knowledge that total chaos will come if the procedure is altered in any way.

That procedure is not, as the misguided male appears to believe, a ritual of superstitious practices; it is a plan for the scientific control of household machinery that is more delicate than a watch and more complex than a factory. Success or failure hinges on the requirement that everything, *everything*, be done at the specified time, in the established way. Nothing could be more shocking than the novice's suggestion that we let something slide for today. Or his question, Why can't that be done later? Or the more revealing, What difference does it make how I do it? Nothing could be more exasperating, either. The engineer was resigned to the necessity of leaving the switchboard in charge of the water boy. But it has now become clear that the water boy is illiterate and more than a little retarded.

And the water boy (who is trying to do some work of his own in stretches of from four to thirteen minutes) is struggling with an internal conflict. He is alarmed by his wife's illness, has firmly in mind that only her staying in

bed will save her and is aghast at her flouting of instruc-
tions. And, great of heart with eagerness to sacrifice his
own work in order to cherish her, he resents her refusal
to credit him with the ability to perform the most unimportant chore.

I had repeatedly to tell Nancy that she would get the
infection in her throat if she didn't stop straining her vocal
cords, that she must go back to bed at once and that I felt
competent to handle, say, the laundry problem. At once
she came to the upstairs railing to ask if I had made a
copy of the laundry list. I told her to go back to bed and
asked whether she couldn't trust a laundry she had been
dealing with for five years. That proved her suspicion
well founded, but the thing was done now, so she con-
tented herself with saying, Well, don't scream if they lose
that pink shirt you're so proud of. Ten minutes later she
got to the railing in time to see me buy two tickets to the
policeman's ball and to say, Sucker! When I pointed out
that she bought them every year, she said that she bought
one, which was just forehanded, but two showed that I
was both a spendthrift and afraid of cops. I said, Go back
to bed. Nancy said, Yes, darling.

By now the rising pressures have changed a woman's
idea of what constitutes a pleasant time. Nancy would
say that I came charging upstairs — which would be putting it unfairly — on discovering that she had washed an
armful of stockings and hung them on a towel rack and
was washing a girdle. When I reminded her that she was
a woman racked with pain, she said she wasn't so sick she
had to put up with dirty clothes. I told her that character

was a fine thing, but intelligence was also well thought of. Understanding that she must now bring logic to bear, Nancy said that when you have a virus infection, nothing you do will make you get well any faster, and that she had already done the intelligent thing — she had had Joe in to look her over. I said, Joe told you to stay in bed. Nancy said, Oh, *Joe!* You can't expect me to pay attention to what he says. It's his job to talk that way. I committed another error by saying that Joe's medical directions were going to cost me ten dollars, and that if she went on disregarding them, he would be back with a long needle and would painfully insert in her some nine dollars worth of aureomycin. Nancy said, Goodness, we can't afford that, the way you squander money on dance tickets. But to pacify me she was willing to use more elementary logic. She said, You must admit that I know what's good for me a lot better than Joe ever could, and besides, I'm doing exactly what he told me to. When he said to stay in bed, he meant I was not to go downstairs, and I haven't, not even once — now, have I? But what silly nonsense it is, she added, this medical superstition that you have to stay upstairs!

This should reveal to anyone, though it never does to a husband, that there is no escape from logic.

However, after trying on the blouse she bought last week but hadn't had a chance to wear yet, Nancy did go back to bed. After a while she called down that it was lunchtime and that she felt up to an egg and some toast and marmalade. She gave me simple directions on how to boil an egg and use the toaster, and was relieved to find that I was able to follow them. Now, with lunch over and her stockings washed and nothing to read, she kept thinking of possibilities she had ignored. She called me to the foot of the stairs to ask if I had washed the lunch dishes. Ten minutes later, it was had I emptied the wastebaskets? Five minutes after that, had I run the vacuum cleaner over the living room? Then, had I phoned in the grocery list she had given me? Since in good faith I intended to do all these things at some convenient time, I truthfully said yes.

Presently, going upstairs to ask which of Caroline's dresses the man from the cleaner's was supposed to take, I found that Nancy had fallen asleep. Perhaps up to this moment a husband has had some chance of coming out with the right answers, but the stampede begins here. She looked very pretty, very small and frail. Touched and deeply disturbed, I thought what misery influenza is and what ghastly things it can lead to. All of them appeared to be certain now, and I watched her breathing for a while, before I tiptoed away, to be absolutely sure she *was* breathing.

Nancy did indeed feel wretched when she woke up — and exactly here we have to understand wherein and why. For that nap is decisive for the sufferer, too; a woman wakes from it to a sudden awareness of the folly she has been committing. In some mysterious way she has let herself be trapped into abandoning the switchboard to this fumbling creature who, however affectionate he may be, is so dreadfully incompetent. All along she has had to ignore a fear that Things Might Go Wrong; but now she knows that They Have Gone Wrong. Dismay, chagrin and shame sweep over her. She cannot deny that she has shown moral weakness; but on the other hand, it is so unlike her that surely she cannot be blamed for it. A trick, a deception, has been played on her. She will deal with that later, but right now she must salvage as much as she can.

Nancy made straight for the children's rooms and found what she had expected to: unmade beds, clothes that must have been kicked around for hours on end, a litter of repulsive objects. After cleaning up this debris, she came out in the hall just too late to stop what was happening at the front door. My first warning that a turn had been rounded was the edge in her voice when she asked how much I had paid that peddler for that broom. Deducting fifty cents from the truth, I told her two dollars. She said that if we used brooms in this house, which we don't any more, they would cost a dollar fifty, but twenty cents would be too much for the ones this crook sells. I told her that the poor guy was blind and she should have some feeling for the afflicted. She said, He takes off those dark glasses when he drives the Cadillac you sentimentalists have bought him. She then held me responsible for the cleaner's failure to call for Caroline's dress. I said that he had called, but not knowing which dress it was, I had told him to come back tomorrow. Nancy said, The poor child wanted it for the high school dance on Friday, but you've fixed that. She added something about the recklessness of taking a nap; but I didn't get all of it, for she vanished into the bedroom.

When I got there, she had put on a frivolous blue bath-robe and some furred slippers. The key to this scene, which is universal in the American home, is the fact that it develops from two irreconcilable sets of anxieties. Here is an anguished husband, wondering whether the way his wife is acting does not mean that she is already delirious, and convinced that her future health, probably her life, depends on his getting her back to bed instantly. And here is the Expert, who must get the wrecked household back on the rails, but is being harassed by a creature — and the one who is responsible for the wreck — jittering at her with some wildly irrelevant nonsense about sick-ness and bed. Since Nancy had uncomplainingly borne so much already, we may understand her feeling a trifle impatient now. She made clear that I was unjust in say-ing she had wanted to stay in bed. I had talked her into it against her judgment; she had gone to bed merely to satisfy me. She acknowledged that this had been weak of her, for she had not been in the least sick — she should not have listened to known hypochondriacs like Joe and me. There had been nothing the matter with her: if there had been, there certainly wasn't now; she felt just fine; would I please, please shut up and leave her alone?

Nancy was unaware that outrage at this atrocious in-justice mingled with my alarm; but she wouldn't have cared, for there was no time to assuage hurt feelings. But she did see that the quickest way to end a galling delay was to prove her point. She told me to shake down the thermometer and she would show me. My relief at this sign of lucidity changed to panic when the thermometer registered 101 degrees. While I was desperately wondering whether Joe could be located at his office or at the hospital, Nancy stood up and reminded me that a thermometer was an undependable instrument that didn't register within three or four degrees of the truth. You know very well, she said, that there really is no such thing as a normal temperature. Besides, thousands of people have a hundred and one all the time.

It would be possible for a man to subdue a delirious woman by main strength, carry her upstairs, and tie her in bed. He has the physical strength. But he is too much her inferior in moral strength. He can only follow her about, aghast with the knowledge that she is insuring herself an oxygen tent if not a coffin. He is under the additional handicap that she catches him off balance when she finally gets downstairs.

For Nancy found the house looking like a photograph that shows the path of a storm. Most of the devastation she saw was created by her own inner vision of catastrophe, but I acknowledge that here and there some slight stimulus to her imagination existed. She found that four quarts of milk had been standing on the back steps all day, that the sink was full of dirty dishes and the coffeepot full of grounds, that someone had waxed the kitchen floor with marmalade, that only a bulldozer could have so torn up the living room in a single day. It is true, too, that one of Tommy's undershirts had somehow got abandoned on the piano and that I would have been wise to bury the fragments of the plate and two drinking glasses I had somehow broken.

During the heroic drive that she must now put on, a woman cannot help suspecting something ominous. The devastation can be explained as the result of the negligence, the clumsiness and the nine-to-five stupidity of men. But the man who impedes the rescue operation now by urging, ordering and imploring her to get back to bed, and doing so in a loud voice somewhat salted with profanity — a man who does not see the stark unreason of talking about health and disease at this moment of crisis must be a little crazed. There is, indeed, proof that he is. He is suffering from a delusion: he thinks she has been sick.

The theory we need is one that will explain a curative agent far more powerful than any miracle drug so far produced in a laboratory. I tend to believe that this agent is exhilaration. For, through the mists of my desperation, I could see that Nancy was having a wonderful time. There is at work a morale, an *esprit*, the buoyancy of an organism perfectly performing its function. There is the satisfaction of the professional who has been summoned to repair what the amateurs have botched, of the battle-toughened regulars on their way to restore the lines from which the green militia have been driven. Meanwhile, the amateur, the militiaman, gets steadily more sodden with despair.

Eventually, she had her head above the rubble and felt secure in pausing for a moment. She put away the dustcloths and the vacuum cleaner, came back through a glistening kitchen to a burnished living room, sat down, lit a cigarette, let a slipper dangle from one bare foot and smiled. It was the smile of the fire chief going back to the station, of the champion coming off the tennis court. The emergency was well in hand now, though of course it was not yet over. The children would require firmness when they got home, for no doubt they had reverted to barbarism while she wasn't looking. But the household was back on the rails; she had taken over the switchboard again, and she could feel a little kindly toward the delusions of a husband. What, indeed, do you do for members of the hypochrondriac sex except treat them with forbearance and reassure them?

In my mind, Joe was already superintending an intern and three nurses while they labored frantically to save her. Raging fever had brought this brightness to her eyes and this color to her cheeks. She said that she was going to get dressed now, and that was delirium. But she lighted a faint hope that her reason might be restored and her life saved when she said, You'd be happier if I let you take my temperature, wouldn't you? Yet even this yielding to sanity was alarming, for it must mean that her strength was ebbing.

I followed her upstairs. With a good humor that would have seemed meek except for the derision in her eyes, she sat quietly while I timed the thermometer for three minutes. I looked at it, put it back in her mouth for another three minutes, and then carefully read it again. The mercury still stood just a trifle below the arrow that points to the normal 98.6 degrees.

Nancy took it from me, looked at it and had the decency to remain grave. You must learn not to get upset about nothing, she said, very gently. If you didn't have such an active imagination, you wouldn't get so frightened. Then I saw a sudden suspicion invade her eyes. Are you feeling bad? she asked me. She came over and put her hand on my forehead. Why, you're all hot! she said. She understood now, and contrition, self-reproach, tender consideration broke out in her. Poor darling, I believe you're getting sick, she said. You go right straight to bed.

6

My Wife Is Many Cooks

THE YEAR has seasons, and Nancy has phases in the imaginative drama whose leading role casts her as caterer, chef and nutritionist. One night you hear the first tree toads, or another night you hear geese going southward overhead, and you know that a turn has been rounded in nature's inscrutable time schedule. Similarly, there comes a day when Nancy returns from the shopping center with a couple of bottles of seventy-five-cent wine, calves' brains, some shallots and a new earthenware pot. A leaf has been turned on that inscrutable calendar, and at our house cooking is going to be French for a while.

The drama of the artist in the kitchen is not continuous, of course. For long periods, dinner is simply the family hour. The menu is suburban seasonal, the cuisine is standard American and Nancy is just a good cook taking the job in her stride. Two children in high school and one in sub-high are a problem only of wholesale food procurement, and a husband's tastes are not a problem at all. At such a time the artist has fallen asleep — and I have never been able to determine what stimulus from within or without breaks that slumber. Let us say that, as all women know, women are the quick-witted and nimble-footed sex, especially when they are wives; and husbands are forever off balance and running several yards behind them. And let us add that Nancy has an appetite that ranks among the most amazing natural phenomena of North America.

I do know that when the artist wakes, Nancy realizes with dismay that we are missing satisfactions which are the birthright of civilized people. The palate and the taste buds were given man for use; not to cultivate their subtleties and harmonies is evidence of dullness or mediocrity. Something of self-reproach goes with this realization, for Nancy admits that our lapse in gracious living is her fault. What are the children expecting for dinner tonight? Doubtless macaroni and cheese, and that classifies them as lingering halfway between savagery and barbarism, from which it is her clear duty to rescue them. What is their father expecting? No doubt, liver and bacon or, even more repulsively, liver and onions; but she acknowledges that in gustatory matters he was born defective, and not much can be done about him. The zealot and crusader have wakened with the artist, however, and Nancy will do what she can. All morning miles pile up on the speedometer while she searches for ingredients she will need — the pigments, so to speak, of the artist's palette. All afternoon she labors in the artist's studio with a devotion that is both fanatical and triumphant. Unfavorable odds and heavy handicaps do not deter her — Nancy's family is about to be restored to civilized eating.

It turns out to be *sole bonne femme*. (Flounder, I remark, moved by a stubborn but injudicious regard for truth.) This means that a half-empty bottle of white wine has been put away on a pantry shelf. Tomorrow we will have *coq au vin*, and a half-used bottle of red wine will join it there. These dishes are merely preliminary experiments the artist makes to assure herself she has not lost her touch; they succeed so easily and brilliantly that Nancy moves on to more impressive things. She produces a complex and laborious sauce (which will add a sherry bottle to the shelf), and this harmonizes with a composition containing broccoli, Parmesan cheese, thin slices of chicken, and I do not know what else. When Caroline, a somewhat reluctant servitor, brings it to the table, it is bubbling magnificently. Nancy informs us that it pleases the ear, the eye and the nostrils, as well as the palate, and that this multiple gratification is the aim of the Cordon Bleu. The next day, rising to still greater heights, she produces *caneton à l'orange*.

Caroline and Dick consume these masterworks as if they were so many hot dogs, for which they have a capacity that has never yet been plumbed. Tommy asks why in heck we never have baked beans, and the artist observes that her husband is displaying his usual dull indifference. Such barbarities, however, cannot mar the artist's appreciation of her work.

Water cress or endive or chicory has replaced the usual lettuce in our salad; odd tastes — mostly fennel, I suppose — have been added to the dressing. Shallots, those café society onions, have shown up in various dishes; we find parsley in the *petits pois;* mushrooms are in nearly everything. Nancy is clearly becoming Marianne, and I judge the role is complete when she provides a staggeringly expensive *paté* to go with my evening cocktail, though she is aware that I prefer peanuts.

It is Marianne who remarks from time to time that in all the United States, or at least in our suburb, really good butter does not exist, and one knows that the basis of the true cuisine is really good butter. At seventy-five cents a bottle, Marianne could afford to drink up those remnants of wine, but thrift is the very center of the French soul; they will turn into the most excellent vinegar, and at no expense. Moreover, observe that her largest kettle stands constantly on the rear burner of the range. Into it goes practically everything left over, and one knows that this is the essence of thrift. Marianne is making potage.

Then, one evening when I enter the house, there is a pervasive odor of vinegar. Now things are going to be marinated, and the artist is named Gretchen. Red cabbage makes its appearance on our table. There will be *Sauerbraten;* there will be *Wiener Schnitzel.* They come as a surprise to a palate that has belatedly adjusted to chicken Marengo; but it would be indiscreet to say so, for the fastidious and discriminating life is versatile. Wherever the delights of eating are to be found, there the artist will seek them. Yet she cannot blind herself to the fact that the father of her children is dismayed by this succession of pancakes, strudels and cheesecakes. Nancy feels no dismay; she can hardly remember enjoying anything so much.

Or, suddenly, the artist remembers sour cream, and borsch re-enters our life. There are blintzes; chicken is now chicken Kiev; presumably it is Sonia in the kitchen. I have said that a husband is a man constantly off balance, a man who hears the starter's pistol only when the partner of his joys and sorrows is fifteen yards down the track. Now, forgetting the Sonia phase and expecting the spareribs to be German, I find that they are sweet-and-sour, which is to say Chinese. Beef is in strips, under a dark sauce thick with peppers. The aroma of vinegar has been replaced by one I manage to identify as soy sauce. If the preceding phases had Nancy shopping all morning, this one has taken her to the city, and she has made an exhilarating tour through Chinatown for bean sprouts, water chestnuts, peanut oil, and litchi nuts. That heaped-up centerpiece is *char shu dan,* or else shrimps with lobster sauce, and again the gracious life is cosmopolitan.

There was no warning, omen, or advance notice when the artist woke. There was none when Marianne became Gretchen or when Sonia became Su-Yin. There is none now. One day I start homeward, and having by now made up some of the ground lost by a husband's slow start, I anticipate one of those miniature triumphs a Cordon Bleu can achieve with veal and white wine. I think pityingly of my friend and neighbor, Pete, who will dine tonight on pork chops fried stiff.

And that evening the Hewes family dines on a casserole of sliced potatoes and leftover beef, the whole sprinkled with cheese, shoved into the oven and disregarded. Yesterday Nancy considered casseroles symbolic of indolence in women and of everything deplorable in the eating habits of America. Tonight she talks about the PTA, and I notice three new novels from the lending library on the living room table. I know that meat loaf, macaroni and cheese, and corned-beef hash will now reappear, that a cycle has been completed. But Nancy devours that casserole as enthusiastically as if it were breast of guinea hen *sous cloche* at the Tour d'Argent.

I have not done justice to the cycle unless I have made clear that Nancy has gone through every phase of it with joyous abandon. In any phase she cooks as enthusiastically as she eats, and if the artist is aware that she is wasting talents which those of finer mold would appreciate, those talents are not wasted on her when she sits down at the table.

It is time now to inquire into the relation of this cycle to other abiding mysteries of the married state — to the hideous injustices habitually inflicted by wives, and to their delusions.

One of the artist's motives is a kindly intent to lead the artist's husband to a more rewarding appreciation of civilized living. But she faces a discouraging fact: he is going to resist enlightenment. Nancy is sure not only that my tastes are dull and plebeian, but that they are grievously limited. What I am really interested in eating, she holds, is overdone steak, French-fried potatoes, and pie à la mode. If I were left to myself, she points out, I would live exclusively on steak, baked beans, ham and eggs, cold cuts and potato salad and an occasional recklessly adventurous serving of buckwheat cakes. She intimates that whatever she may do in the kitchen, it is done to bring light to my darkness, to make richer my pitifully impoverished life.

Men are the idealistic sex: they try to answer women with facts and logic. Wrung by this hideous and willful misrepresentation, I review the entire history of our marriage. I cite innumerable facts, episodes and restaurant bills that prove her wrong. I achieve what I am sure is eloquence; but obviously Nancy hears none of it. An expression that is part pity and part horror comes to her face. Of course, she says, the real tragedy is that you simply aren't interested in food. From her point of view, that is equivalent to a musician's saying someone is tone deaf.

Well, there is a coarse feeder in our household. For Nancy's devotion, skill, and hard labor as an artist I have only admiration. As I have shown, she will spend a whole afternoon preparing that duckling with orange, and frankly, I do not understand how she is able to do it without at least two assistants. She puts into it a zeal for perfection that is beyond praise. I am willing to call this the creative process at work: Nancy has, so to speak, composed a sonata, a symphony, and she has done so with an all-out enthusiasm that touches the heart.

Then she falls to and eats the duckling with the same enthusiasm. The artist has labored so that the gourmet may experience these rare and subtle harmonies. So runs

the theory; but the fact is that in the absence of *caneton
à l'orange,* an onion sandwich will produce the same harmonies. Nancy will eat a boiled egg or indeed a dill pickle
with the same surprised and passionate abandon. And this
fact, I point out to her, brings a new light to bear on the
nature of civilized living. Roast goose Bohemian is doubtless very fine — but what if a cheese-on-rye will do as
well? And if a cheese-on-rye will produce this absorption,
this charming sparkle of the eye, this soft pinkness of the
cheek, am I to call it the love of gracious living or simple
gluttony? Admittedly, the male taste may be hard to
please, I say, but when you compare it with a taste that
can attain ecstasy with a soda cracker, which is the coarse
one?

Also, there is an injustice so overwhelming as to produce
despair. On the day we were married, Nancy weighed
one hundred and seventeen pounds. Today she weighs
one hundred and sixteen pounds. In twenty years of un-
limited eating she has varied no more than the sixteen
ounces of that single pound. And she eats — she has
always eaten — on a scale that would maintain a platoon
in combat.

I have suggested to her that what we must recognize
here is a sluggish and inefficient metabolism, able to convert only a small portion of this food into energy and none
at all into fat. Whereas, I point out, *my* metabolism performs with an efficiency that is the admiration of physiol-
ogists. Five pounds will add themselves to the weight
my vanity and my doctor have set for me, if I permit
myself as much as a second slice of any true gastronome's

delight. This admirable physiological system functions always at high gear and maintains itself on a slice of rare beef and a spoonful of broccoli. It will extract from a single lamb chop more than Nancy's insensitive system can get from a meal that begins with thick soup and progresses to *crème brulée* by way of a rich dark sauce on the beef and hollandaise on the asparagus.

In the face of these facts, I said to Nancy, it is both arrogant and foolish to pretend that your sluggish metabolism implies spiritual fineness, and it is cruelly unjust to denounce me as defective when I am merely trying to keep your husband from looking like a cartoon of a Wall Street broker. The truth is that I am the sensitive and —

Here I realized that I was talking to myself. Nancy was gone. For a long moment there was silence, and then from the kitchen, clear and unmistakable, came the sound of a refrigerator door's opening, the gurgle of milk from a bottle, the crunch of soda crackers. . . .

7

The Zippered Egg Boiler

EVERY few months, the Sunday paper runs an article that tells us mankind will eventually be destroyed by its own machines. These prophecies must all be written by bachelors who have spent their lives in institutions that are safely barricaded against the feminine mind. If they knew women at all, they would not worry; for as long as there are women, and especially wives, machines haven't a chance. Perhaps machines will, sometime, be foolish enough to start a war with women, but they will never be good enough to win it.

The same fantasy of doom is common in a form of literature to which my younger son Tommy is passionately devoted — science-fiction. Here, a favorite nightmare is one in which machines have reached such perfection that they form a conspiracy and enslave mankind. Nancy reacts to this with a sound resembling a snicker and so goads Tommy into protest.

But, Ma, he says, it's *true!* We've already got machines that have *memory,* Ma. Just turn 'em on, and in ten seconds they solve problems that the whole Harvard faculty couldn't solve in a hundred years.

I know dear, Nancy says, and someday the one at Harvard will marry the one at Columbia, and soon there'll be a lot of little adding machines playing in the back yard. But the Hewes family hasn't got one yet, and meanwhile, how about doing your algebra all by yourself?

Observe that Nancy has automatically derided an idea that Tommy takes with complete seriousness. Tommy believes there are going to be increasingly ingenious machines because, as a male, he believes in Progress. Nancy, who may be called Everywoman, does not believe in Progress, and therefore she finds his idea just funny. If Tommy were to commit the folly of pointing out to her that her house is full of machines which she uses with admirable, if unconscious, mastery, she would tell him this simply is not so and, anyway, they are just gadgets that fascinate his father.

I point out that, though these gadgets are exquisite and beautiful objects, admirable in themselves, they were all invented in order to free women from backbreaking, soul-stunting hand labor so that women could remain lovely and live graciously. Not at all, Nancy tells me. They only make work for women, and men have thought up this labor-saving pretense in order to dignify their incurable love of toys.

We have already seen two items in Everywoman's attitude toward machines: They are funny or, at least, frivo-

lous, and they are toys. That, however, is only the beginning, for this attitude is a complex thing, and women
cross you up by changing it to suit their whims. Another
element in it we may call the So-Far-and-No-Farther principle. See how this operates in Everywoman's treatment
of that marvelous machine, the family automobile.

It is impossible to imagine a woman feeling an emotion
about an automobile. A man may think it beautiful, he
may fall in love with it, he may get angry at it, but always
he respects it as something having its own needs and ways,
something to be treated with tender consideration. To
a woman, it belongs to the class of machines that can be
called simply objects — inert, without significance or
identity. She is here and wants to go over there. Out in
front of the house is an object that will take her. She gets
into the object, performs certain operations and it takes
her there. She leaves it at the curb, and it ceases to exist
till she wants to go somewhere else.

Everywoman has learned to accept the fact that she
won't get there unless the car has gas, which means that
gas must be put into it, from time to time, just as you put
the woolens away when hot weather comes. But So-Far-
and-No-Farther — her understanding does not run to oil.
If I were to say, Nancy, what are your associations with
the word oil? I would most probably get something like
this: Texas — Nieman-Marcus — scoop-neck blouse. Or,
Spots — jersey to cleaner's — no, buy new one. Her joyous and disdainful mind would never produce such an
association as: one-thousand-mile change. Nor would her
mind encompass such important matters as the engine,

the transmission, the electric system, the brakes, or the tires. Maybe a car does have parts, but they are none of her affair.

What happens when something goes wrong — the battery fails, or there is a sudden knocking sound and the car coasts to a stop? A man is instantly concerned about the car, which is suffering some ailment. A women is affronted, almost intolerably insulted — not by the car but by the male sex which invented it, including her husband who bought it. This object was supposed to get her where she wanted to go, and it has failed. An object that does not do what it is supposed to do is no good at all, and what business do men have inventing such abominable frauds? Here are two further principles: Machines-Are-Men's-Fault and Unless-It's-Perfect-It's-No-Good-at-All.

I remind Nancy that history knows of one machine invented by a woman, the circular saw. At this, the bridge of Nancy's nose wrinkles scornfully, and she creates a twofold impression: this solitary female inventor was a traitor to her sex; also, she was probably led to her unnatural act by watching a man trying to invent the saw. There came a point when she could stand his male ineptness no longer; so she showed him how.

We may thus add disdain and patronizing superiority to the components of a woman's attitude toward machines or to that class of machines that are merely objects — automobiles and the like.

There is, however, a whole other group she thinks of as Machines, with a capital M, and to these she attributes a kind of rudimentary life or, at least, consciousness. A

Machine has motives, and they are evil ones; it is not to be trusted. Thus, to Nancy an elevator is an object, something at hand that will take her to the tenth floor. But she will never take an escalator if there is any way of not taking it. She explains that it looks like a stairway but it moves. Obviously, stairways are not meant to move; so there is something dishonest and tricky about one that does.

This explanation sounds like pure subterfuge, and I say so. Nancy says, indignantly, as the person who has to pay for my stockings, I should think you'd appreciate my trying to keep them from getting snagged. There you have it: Nancy knows the dim, brooding, malicious mind of an escalator snaps to attention when she appears. Boy, it tells itself, here comes a pair of 15-denier, amber-beige, full-fashioned nine-and-a-halves. At least a dollar sixty-nine. Whoopee!

I cannot imagine, no one can imagine, how a stocking could get snagged on an escalator; but if I should try to point out certain fallacies in her argument, Nancy would only counter by reminding me of The Case of Sarah's Washing Machine.

It was Pete's washing machine, really, Pete being an ardent devotee of Progress, who loves any kind of meshing gears — and, of course, he is fond of Sarah, too. At praiseworthy expense, he installed a washing machine that filled and emptied itself, started and stopped according to its own judgment, and performed so many other skillful, intelligent actions that you even expected to see it sewing on buttons and telling Pete blue shirts weren't becoming to him. This machine was deeply satisfying to him, as it would be to any poetic soul, and for some time, the neighbors gathered in his basement on Saturdays to hear him lecture on it while it sang away at its job.

Sarah adjusted herself to the marvel with no more than the usual skepticism and resistance, and for a time all went well. But a day came when a cleaning woman loaded it with eight or ten times as many sheets, curtains, and for all I know, living room rugs as it was intended to deal with at one time. (In a woman's philosophy of the machine, why not? A washing machine is supposed to do the washing, isn't it?) The machine did its loyal best, but it probably made a lot of noise — Nancy reports that it growled and roared terrifyingly.

I gathered that the cleaning woman's scream brought Sarah down from her second-floor dusting and that Sarah's scream brought our ever helpful Nancy over on the run. This appalled sisterhood stood at the top of the basement stairs while the machine went on trying to do the job and, on Nancy's word, strode up and down the basement, presumably lashing its tail. You know, as well as I do, that it was simply shaking on its now overloaded legs; but in the minds of three women, it had gone beserk.

Understand, to Everywoman there is always this possibility with Machines: Since they have consciousness, they can go crazy. Through Nancy's mind flashed the thought that we have police for such emergencies and that, if she could get them there in time, they would shoot the monster. And then Tommy arrived. The women's clamor had roused him from important affairs, and

he had come over to see what was going on. He said, Aw,
nuts — women! and went downstairs and turned off the
current.

No man is bright enough to tell in advance whether
something is an object or a Machine, but if it is the latter,
there is always the possibility that its dim mind may flame
into rebellion. How does Nancy know that a toaster may
not turn and attack her? That is, a pop-up toaster — the
kind she was used to as a girl is just an object. Now, this
brings us to another fundamental part of women's attitude
toward machines, involving both their instinctive con-
servatism (or absolute disbelief in Progress) and a nostalgia for their childhood. And, since it applies especially
to household machines, it is bewildering and saddening
to husbands.

Toward any new appliance, including even those she
herself has bought, Everywoman's attitude falls into various stages. First, protest: It's silly and useless and she
doesn't want it. Second, indulgence: It's doing things the
hard way, but if her husband gets so much pleasure from
having her use this new toy, she will string along. Third,
acceptance: It doesn't exist; it has become an object, she
is using it regularly, she has always used it, and if anybody mentions it, why, it was her idea all along. But, of
course, it's no good.

For instance: I brought home a fascinating egg boiler,
a device that, once set, emits pleasing jets of steam and
turns itself off when the eggs reach the degree of hardness
or softness you prefer. Nancy ridiculed it as a gadget
and, after (at my insistence) open-mindedly using it once,

refused to have anything to do with it. She said it was a waste of time; she could boil eggs in a saucepan much faster. Stubbornly, I timed both operations. They came out practically a tie; but, since you have to bring the water in a saucepan to a boil first, my lovely thing won by a few seconds.

Nancy then argued that the device did not boil eggs, it steamed them, which is true. When I pointed out that steam is only boiling water in a different form and that both produce the same result in the eggs, the court found against me. Who, she demanded, who ever heard of steaming eggs? (Meaning: We boiled them when I was a girl.) That settled it, and for some months the device went unused, except on mornings when Tommy or Dick and I got our own breakfasts. Then, one day, Tommy, for secret purposes of his own, borrowed the sandglass — just like the one Grandma had — by which Nancy had always timed eggs. He lost it, and ever since then, Nancy has used the egg steamer as a matter of course. I repeat: as a matter of course. It's just there, she isn't aware of it, she would tell you she has always used an egg steamer. She would also tell you that boiling eggs in a saucepan is simpler, faster and better; but if my device should wear out, she would buy a new one.

This, I point out, is a cultural lag. All day long women employ the countless horsepower the burning vision of men has put at their disposal, yet mendaciously assert, first, that they do no such thing and, second, that Grandma's way was much better. The sandglass was a machine, I point out, with no hope of getting anywhere. A clock

is a machine. A bicycle (and this Nancy resolutely refuses to believe) was a machine when you rode one in
your happy girlhood. All right, Nancy says, take that
sheep-shearing gadget that sets my teeth on edge every
morning, wailing in the bathroom like a homeless and off-
tune ghost. I'll bet it doesn't shave you any better than
Grandpa's forty-cent straightedged razor with the lovely
carving of Niagara Falls on the handle. And, she adds
as a clincher, your gadget doesn't even have a carving of
Niagara Falls.

How, a mere man wonders, can a woman ignore the
tremendous emancipation modern machines have brought
her, the deliverance from hard labor that has kept her
hands soft, her figure straight and slim (supposedly) and
the arches of her feet unfallen?

That's easy. She can ignore them by saying the gadgets
men force on her increase her work instead of reducing
it, and anyway, this is irrelevant since what we really
have here is a lot of toys for adult male children.

Take a six-year-old boy, Nancy says. How do you fill
him with delight at Christmas? You give him a gadget
that lets a marble slide down something with a lovely
noise, hit something with a bang, and knock another
marble into the air and through a hole — with a bang.
All day long, the little cherub will play with this lovely,
lovely thing, will crow over it and brag about it. Twenty-
five years later, what does he do? He demonstrates his
love for his wife by presenting her with a gadget that
peels onions — it peels them fully half as well as she can
without it, it doesn't take more than twice as long, and

it shuts itself off with a bang. What he really loves is that bang, and that's why a woman's house is full of gadgets that don't do what they're supposed to and have to be washed — automatic, self-winding, reciprocating toys he wants her to call tools.

But at twelve, I tell her, this same boy will take an old alarm clock, some pulleys, and a hundred feet of wire and construct a device that shuts his window, while he lies in bed ravished by the delight of knowing *it works.* This male pleasure in proving it works is the sole reason you are not, at this moment, clad in a rabbit skin, crouching over a fire of twigs in a cave and gnawing a piece of half-cooked mammoth.

And, when that twelve-year-old is twenty-five, he will invent an electric iron that turns itself off when you answer the telephone. . . .

No, Nancy says firmly, there won't ever be an iron that turns itself off; that's much too sensible an idea for a man to put into a toy. I tell her it is simplicity itself, even I could do it; all it requires is a thermostat. With kindly condescension, she says, Thermostats are on the living room wall.

This creative spirit we were speaking of, I say, he's now thirty years old. He has moved on from the marble and the window closer and the thermostatically controlled iron. Now, one glorious morning, lo, an oil furnace! No more shoveling coal, no more carting out ashes, no more smudging your rugs with grimy footprints. Progress has reached a new high. And all because of this splendid thrill forever denied the reactionary sex, *it works.*

Not when a cold spell comes, Nancy says. It gives up in despair, shuts itself off with a bang, and we all get pneumonia. Say what you will about that fire in the cave, it used to keep us warm, it didn't need a thermostat, and it never went bang. There's a lot to be said for house-keeping in a cave.

Having no more time to waste on the absurdities of male logic, Nancy goes out into the kitchen, whence there presently issues the busy murmur of a food mixer whip-ping cream. Nancy calls upstairs to Caroline directing her to straighten up her room. Presently, a swish and a purr mean that Nancy has put the dishwasher to work, and soon I hear a swoosh that shows she has pressed a button and persuaded the oven to light itself.

I go out to the back yard and stretch out the garden hose to its full length and attach a new sprinkler I bought on my way home. I can only say it is a distinguished work of art. Slowly, inch by inch, it travels up the hose and so eventually covers the whole lawn. I turn on the water and stand admiring its poetic movement and the rainbows the summer sunset makes in its whirling jets. Nancy's head and shoulders come through the kitchen window. Won-derful, she says, the poetic spirit of immortal boyhood thought that up, and *it works!* Oh, lovely; it keeps you from breaking your back lifting half a pound of sprinkler and putting it over there. But when does it go bang?

When I return to the house, the happy song of the vacuum cleaner is drifting down from Caroline's room. It is evident that Nancy is freshening for dinner, for I hear the shower, and presently there is a thump in the basement which means the water heater has gone on. In the kitchen, a ticking promises that in a given number of minutes a bell will ring and summon Nancy to turn the roast. And yet, there isn't a single machine in the house — only a couple of silly gadgets her husband has brought home to play with. I realize, then, that the war between women and machines isn't even going to get started. It can't; the machines are out of luck. Women won't so much as acknowledge that they exist.

Nancy comes down wearing some charming yellow and green fluff that would not have been called a dress in Grandma's day. She turns around and backs toward me. Zip me up, she says. I don't think I can conscientiously, I tell her. I would be helping you betray your beliefs. This dress has to be thrown away. Don't you realize that a zipper is a machine? Nonsense, Nancy says. If it were, it would zip itself up with a bang. And, where's its thermostat?

MEN, WOMEN AND WRITERS

8

Men, Women and Eight Cylinders

OUR learned brethren, the psychologists, seem not to have observed that we all drive automobiles. But we do, and it behooves them to take note of the fact. Just as an experiment, a team of them ought to spend an hour on a highway, or five minutes by the traffic circle at the edge of town. They would discover that the motorist's mind is the most fascinating wilderness left for them to explore.

Any serious treatise on the normalities (if any) and abnormalities of the driver's mind would run to twice as many volumes as the encyclopedia; but that is no excuse for failing to make a start right here. And we had better steer straight into the sex differences. (Let's not ask whether men or women are the better drivers. The insurance companies say that women are, but I don't agree. It's a question of what "better" means before the crash.)

Women are unromantic, unimaginative and impatient of pretense. They are practical, logical and rational. As one consequence, they have little regard for theoretical formalities like traffic regulations. Why, certainly, she saw the arrow saying this is a one-way street. But no car was coming down it, so there was no reason she shouldn't drive up it. Besides, it was silly to make this particular street one way, and we are never going to get better government if citizens go on supinely accepting civic imbecility. As for driving sixty-five miles an hour where the sign says forty is the legal limit — now, look here: in order to drive safely, we have to use our heads; surely the Highway Commission doesn't want us to abandon our common sense and intelligence when we are driving a car.

This is a clear, logically coherent point of view, which the woman driver is perfectly willing to explain to any cop who may stop her. That willingness is one of two reasons a woman gets stopped much less often than a man and, when stopped, gets far fewer tickets. She knows, to begin with, that it is all the cop's fault, catches him off balance, usually before he can say a word, and puts it to him squarely that nothing is at stake except his own stupidity. Long experience has taught him the futility of arguing with a woman armed with righteousness. He is lucky if he gets a chance to explain who he thought the offending party was.

You know what the other reason is. She is a realist: she knows that guile was given to women to be used, and she throws her charm at the cop with a blatancy that would shame a high school girl making a freshman date her. Or her chilled-steel brain makes her so dewily repentant for her helpless-little-me brainlessness in driving through the red light that the cop can only end by assuring her no harm was done and she was probably right at that.

Women know that God and the male sex have endowed them with certain preferential rights. When a woman suddenly cuts across three lanes of traffic in order to make a left turn, her reason for doing so is entirely different from a man's. She had to make a left turn, so she exercised her privilege of doing what she pleases. The men who have jammed on their brakes and are swearing at her are making fools of themselves; they are the same men who invariably stand back to let her enter an elevator first. Besides, men know very well that women think faster and have quicker reflexes. They should therefore be prepared for a woman to jump the gun at a light, dart past on the right side, or stop dead without signaling. She can take care of herself, and if men can't, they ought not to be driving cars. Suppose she did cut out of line going up that hill? She was getting where she wanted to.

No one ever saw a woman tenderly polishing a car or grieving because she had found a dent in a fender. A woman is incapable of feeling love for an automobile. She understands that it is a machine, and she treats it as one, with unalloyed contempt. Hence, of course, those bitter scenes with a husband whose one ewe lamb has been maltreated. (For heaven's sake, I never have to put a quart of oil in the refrigerator, do I? The vacuum cleaner never needs water in the battery. Why should the car?) Hence, too, much of her behavior on the road. Brakes are made to stop the car with; she therefore requires them to stop it at any speed and in any condition of road or weather. Shift into second going up a hill? Second is what you use when starting; a car in motion travels in third. If it shudders or stalls, then it is just a bad machine, and the engineers ought to make one that won't.

The automobile psychology of women is almost infinitely less interesting than that of men. To a woman, an automobile is just a wheeled vehicle used for transportation; to a man it is alive, miraculous and sacred. It is his seven-league boots, his flying carpet, his chariot armed with scythes. It is his lance, sword, six-gun, brass knuckles and poisoned arrow. But what counts much more, it is his child. And what counts most of all, it is his one true love, more beautiful, more seductive, more tenderly to be cherished than any woman. Love is the strongest of the forces that transform a man when he gets into an automobile, and love always makes a man act many roles.

It makes him, for instance, an uncompromising idealist. There is a code of automobile driving just as there is a code of Christian ethics, and he is fanatical about its being obeyed. A car cuts from one lane into another, and then that car and our driver's stop side by side at a red light. A kind of blasphemy has been committed, his duty is to speak, and he leans out the window and explains the other driver's sin. He may explain pityingly, sternly, or passionately, depending on how strong his reverence is. And not only when the sinner can hear him. Listen to his monologue as he sees the ideal violated all day long: "Step on it. Don't be afraid" — the car ahead is hesitat-

ing, whereas ideal driving must not hesitate and he himself is always decisive. "Don't cut that curve blind" —
"You can't make it, you fool" — "Well, make up your
mind. Which way?" — "Sister, you're going to die young"
— "Look, I haven't got all day" — "Who passed your driving test?" — "*Now,* pass him, now!" At his desk and in
his home, this is a soft-spoken man, much concerned lest
he hurt someone's feelings. But behind the wheel he is a
censor of manners and morals, exasperated, resigned, in
despair. Mankind will not live up to the miracle of being
privileged to drive, and moment by moment its tragic
failure tortures him.

His own honor and his love's give him other roles. A
mild man, I repeat, even a meek man; but a tiger sleeps
in him, and sleeps lightly. Offer no indignity to him or his
car, for he can instantly be the giant roaring from his
castle, or Sir Lancelot defending love's ideal, or Joe Louis.
If you get away before he does when the light changes,
your pride must be humbled. His maleness has been
roused; he steps on the accelerator and shoots past you,
and now who is master? Part of that rage is not only of
the male but of the hunter, the courtly knight, the lone
prowler of the wilderness. You are the Enemy, you have
paid for your presumption, and in his ears is the sound
of bugles blowing victory. Or did you foolishly believe
your nerves steadier or your courage more flinty than his?
You must have, for you have just now passed him. So,
honking a defiance like that of a moose ready to give
battle, he pulls even with you. Now we shall see whose
nerve will hold, who will cravenly drop back at a curve

or where the road narrows. Beneath the commonplace appearance of this mild man, the champion is always ready for the test, and the champion knows that moments come once in a while when all must be risked for the sake of valor.

But you have also outraged the lover. That ugly thing you drive — did you suppose it could pass his beloved? O fool, O reckless one, will he not avenge the slight? You did not know the spirit of his car, the power that lies hidden beneath her beautiful hood, the scornful grace with which she can sweep past your slattern. He and his car are a true marriage, a spiritually deep union: it is Antony and Cleopatra who have shamed you on U.S. 5.

Meanwhile, his strong language has ceased to be the reproof of the instructor in ethics. These are a fighter's expletives and epithets now, the language of a champ. Sometimes the champ shouts them at the Enemy, when a stop light gives them a moment for combat. The air is seared with them, and "You wanna make something of it?" This is full male belligerence, the heavyweight shuffling his shoes in the rosin, the bull entering the ring. But the light lasts for only forty seconds, and no one can stage a death struggle when twenty other cars are blowing their horns. The champ hurls a final oath, shifts gears, is off like the arrow of fate, shoots into a narrowing space between cars, shoots out of it, charges headlong at a car coming toward him, swerves into line in front of one whose brakes are shrieking and scatters others till the hills hide him. The heavyweight has knocked you out; the bull has gored you and is trampling your corpse.

Gradually the adrenalin poured into his bloodstream is absorbed again and he is just a man driving a car. But must we not decide that life has given him a high moment? At home and the office timidities engulf him, he gets no chance to soar, he knocks out no one and has never trampled a single corpse. Nevertheless, his true self is not timorous; he was born to swagger like D'Artagnan, smiling, whistling a careless tune, hand on his sword hilt, among armed bullies who dare not meet his eye. Thus seen, even the cigar-smoking, shirt-sleeved, derby-hatted, yelling, and horn-blowing maniac who comes at you on the wrong side of the road round a curve at seventy miles an hour — even he is splendid and forlorn. Half a tankful of gas has given him, will give any man, the hero's role in a great drama. His car makes him a free, enfranchised citizen of fantasy land and gives his dream a deed. Yet this is the part of dreamland that has the sun on it, and we must remember that parts of it are in the dark; that the poet and hero at the wheel lives sometimes in a nightmare.

One fantasy is particularly fascinating. I suppose it touches most drivers lightly, but in some percentage it becomes urgent. Let us say ten per cent and then divide them equally; half are the A's, the other half the B's. The A's, who are the more easily understood, are devil-ridden by the Car Ahead. There it is, a bright green coupé fresh from the dealer's floor, smooth and graceful, effortless, flirtatious as the twitch of a skirt, disdainful as a snub. We have already seen that this car may be mocking our driver, or challenging his manhood, or insulting his true

love. But there is something else about it, something very
mysterious, and an additional motive impels him to pass
it. In fact, it must be passed — a will from the depths of
his mind tells him so. He passes it, and he has vindicated
himself, but also he has appeased or exorcised some dread.
And almost at once there is again the Car Ahead, this
time a ramshackle old wreck. It could be neither a chal-
lenge to him nor an affront; but again his muscles tighten
and the same dark will commands him. He breathes more
easily as he passes it, a tension is reduced — but there is
still the Car Ahead. Old or new, dull or shiny, fifty feet
from his bumper or twinkling over a rise three miles away,
there it is and it must be passed or — Or what? Or something dire will happen. The Car Ahead is a scud of witch's
fire, a Flying Dutchman of the highway, a malign and
evil thing that threatens him so long as he is behind it.

The B's recognize more clearly than the A's what this
mysterious danger is. The day is sunny and green, sweet
with the scent of apple blossoms. The road is beautiful,
a series of long slopes and sweeping curves, four lanes
wide, not patrolled, with little traffic. But this driver is a
B, and his eyes are forever flicking across the rear-vision
mirror. His vigilant glance detects an oncoming shimmer
far behind him, and warmth vanishes from the sunlight,
peace from his mind. He steps on the gas, and his car
bolts down the highway. If a hill shuts out that baleful
glimmer, or if he really sinks it below the horizon, he can
be tranquil again. But not for long. Other cars enter
from side roads he has passed. Or, materializing out of
nowhere, a car appears so close behind him that his true

love must put all her gallant heart into a burst of speed to make them both safe. It does not matter how many cars are ahead of him; the Car Behind must not catch up. If it ever did — well, what would happen if you ever came face to face with the thing you hear sobbing at midnight in the woods?

The Car Ahead and the Car Behind are supernatural. They are brushed with an infernal phosphorus, and behind the wheel of each sits a creature with pointed, furry ears, red eyes and curving tusks. The A's are luckier than the B's. The moment they draw even with the Car Ahead, the demon changes into a tired, bald man, and his baleful car into a somewhat battered 1946 coupé. The A's, that is, can exorcise the evil and feel the sane wind again and see the good sun — for a while. But the B's must flee headlong forever, their necks crawling with fear of that hellish snout. I can't tell you what happens when the Car Ahead is driven by a B and the Car Behind by an A, when the driver who *must* pass has to overtake the one who *must not* be passed. That, I suppose, is what we read about on the first page of our morning newspaper.

Is it not clear by now why women drivers are dull stuff to a psychologist? Prosaic things, bent only on humdrum practical affairs, using a car to get from here to there, they miss almost everything that makes motoring worth while. Take that clogged ten minutes at the intersection of two main arteries or at a bridge that has been raised to let a boat go through, with cars backed up for a mile each way. Does a woman feel that the order of nature has been violated? Is she so intolerably affronted by fate and the defective human race that she must have self-expression? Not at all. She switches off the engine, lights a cigarette, and turns her mind to tomorrow's shopping list.

A thousand horns are blowing, but not a single one of them is being blown by a woman. What you hear is a symphony, an oratorio, a chant, bugles ordering the charge, and an assertion of the undaunted spirit of mankind breasting a hostile world. D'Artagnan is in there blowing a horn, and so is King Arthur, so are Richard Coeur de Lion, Kit Carson, Paul Bunyan, Jack the Giant Killer — every intrepid spirit, every daredevil of romance.

Thus psychologists must see the male driver. Thus women must see him, too — and so, especially, must highway departments, legislatures, engineers, insurance companies and all of us who drive cars. When we make roads or laws for the woman driver, when we see one coming toward us, we need remember only that she is a hard-boiled individualist who is bound somewhere on a mission of importance and is going to get there regardless. But what we must remember about the man driver is that his car is Isolde, Deirdre, Héloise. That when he gets behind the wheel, he becomes seven feet tall, with shoulders like a Notre Dame guard and fists the size of hams. That Excalibur is hanging from his belt and a light machine gun lies across his knees. That when he slips into high gear, he is off to the wars, to the unmapped wilderness and the uncharted seas. Admire him, watch him — and give him lots of room.

9

Derbies Are Male

A MORE or less innocent male amusement comes from showing women how silly their clothes look in snapshots of ten, twenty, thirty, or even three years ago. Mr. Webster has probably used it in "How to Torture Your Wife," for it is a dependable way to torture any woman — the girls always fall for it. Don't tell me we ever wore coats down to the *ground!* Just look at that waistline — it's a foot below my hips. Knee-length formal evening dresses — well, at least we'll never do that again. Imagine! — pointed shoes — stockings with lace inserts — tricorne hats — those semi-bustles — those piped jackets with pointed lapels — those chunky shoulder pads. There is some nostalgia in women's laughter when they see what queer clothes they were wearing then, whenever that was. But there is more mortification in it and that is what the amused husband is aiming at. For men have stable personalities: fashion has no hold on them. Also, they are rational and the irrationality of women's clothes amazes them.

I can remember all the styles I have just listed, but I can't remember any men who averted their gaze when a woman who was wearing them came down the sidewalk. I can remember starched shirtwaists, hobble skirts, slashed skirts, the periodic rise and fall of the hemline, heaven knows how many kinds of panels and floating drapery. They looked fine to me, they looked natural and attractive, and the fact that I remember them would seem to establish something. They looked fine to the husband who now roars with laughter over them, too. I do not myself remember high-necked, white-striped black bathing suits with skirts halfway to the ankle over bloomers all the way there, but I've seen photographs of them. I note that the men in those photographs are always looking at the women, which is the point I've just made. My next point is this: observe the bathing suits the men have on.

I was in college when the F. Scott Fitzgerald age began. One day my roommate came to a daring and momentous decision. For two years he had held back from a radical innovation, sure that the reckless minds who were pioneering it were endangering the structure of society. Now he decided that established standards were secure, that we pioneers were really making life richer and fuller. So he went out and bought a pair of what, as late as 1920, were still called "low shoes." But he probably could not have brought himself to buy them except that many of us who were wearing low shoes had fought in the first war and so could not be suspected of effeminacy.

Up to then shoes were sissy if they did not lace over the ankle. Or button there — we all had buttonhooks, we even had folding ones to carry in the breast pocket. Brown shoes were acceptable, but only just. The soundest minds, for instance people who wanted to be bank tellers, stuck to black. And the cashier had more confidence in you if they laced halfway up and hooked the other half.

About that time women, or rather girls, were horrifying newspaper editors and delighting Dress Reformers (a species of female whose clothes were designed on philosophical principles and who never looked good in anything) by abandoning petticoats altogether and, so the editors claimed, taking off their corsets before going to dances. An Emancipation was at flood tide. For years philosophers had been exhorting women to get rid of the enslaving, unhygienic, health-destroying, waist-and-soul-constricting corset, but they were shocked and scared when women took them up. Society, morals and the home were going to be in ruins by September. There was so much uproar about corsets left in the checkroom that the corresponding male Emancipation got no headlines.

It had been under way for some years. For generations there had been only two kinds of male underwear, union suits and matched sets of undershirts and drawers. They were knitted and form-fitting, except where they bagged. They were fine for men who worked in the open during the winter. But it took a long time for the male sex to admit that they were uncomfortable indoors and during hot weather, and a longer time to decide that discomfort was not indissolubly linked with respectable citizenship.

By the time I reached high school age the glacierlike progress of male thinking had got us to lightweight knitted underwear and to models that ended above the elbow and at the knee. There were, however, still shirts, drawers and union suits. But now there was a sudden, sharp advance. A manufacturer began to make knitted underwear with little holes in it for ventilation. The invincible prudery of men makes it unlikely that you will ever find a snapshot of your husband wearing this stuff, but if you do you will have a formidable weapon for the counterattack. Nobody could look at it now without rolling on the floor.

It was the track team that finally got us into intelligent and comfortable underwear, underwear which if not powerfully esthetic does not make a candid bystander jeer. For years the track team had been wearing what were called running pants and sleeveless shirts of the kind that women called vests. Dauntless experimenters found that the garments made more comfortable underwear than union suits and eventually the rest of us followed their example — after a period during which they were hitched together for dignity's sake. And what had kept us so long in knitted drawers? The master dictator of male fashions — fear of being thought effeminate. Much of women's underwear was loose-fitting and ended at the shoulder and the knee; to wear anything that resembled it in any way would be sissy. But no one could doubt the masculinity of hurdlers, shot-putters and pole-vaulters. Once that liberating thought broke on us we felt secure in shorts.

There is no length to which my sex will not go to prevent that suspicion of effeminacy. And yet when men
thought low shoes and light underwear sissy they were
wearing nightshirts without a qualm. A nightshirt is only
a nightgown on a man but it wasn't effeminate till we
took up pajamas. And one remembers a remark of Ches-
terton's. He said that when men wanted to symbolize the
dignity of their most solemn callings, they put on skirts —
the priest's vestments, the judge's and the scholar's robes.
(He forgot the kilts that the Highlanders have always
fought in.) We are even more logical about cosmetics,
which we never use. Our face powder comes in a can
labeled "Talcum for Men," and the sole purpose of our
perfume is to soothe the face after the exclusively male
act of shaving. Manufacturers reassure us further by
saying that they have added hormones to the perfume
and that the scent comes from the harness-room, the hunt-
ing lodge or the men's bar. Never suppose that brushless
shaving cream is a depilatory.

Come back to those old snapshots. If the harem skirt
looks silly now, take a look at the man who is admiring it.
I was going to direct your attention first to his derby but
I guess we will have to call hats a draw. It appears to be
impossible to design headgear that doesn't look silly.
Women's hats looked silly when they consisted of stuffed
birds nesting among ribbons beside a bunch of grapes,
and they look silly now when they are half a handful of
anything. A derby looked silly but, whether square or
rounded, black or gray or tan, it didn't look any sillier
than a topper, a Homburg, a boater, a pork-pie or the con-

servative model with a crease down the middle that I
bought yesterday. Besides, derbies had a stern logic of
a kind that women never had to take into account when
they bought hats. They were part of the manhood ritual.
A Sioux could not wear a feather in his hair till he had
been on a war party, and a man could not wear a derby
till he came of age.   .

But take the shirt. Eventually we found that the social
order would still stand if we chucked starched bosoms,
but we held on to cuffs and collars for a long, long time,
much longer than the irrational sex stuck to whalebone.
We still wear boiled shirts with those easy and eye-en-
gaging outfits some of us put on for formal occasions —
and if you want to see how rigorous logic can be, take a
look at a man in tails or a cutaway. He has never known
what to do with the tails, the boiled shirt bows out and
squeaks, his vest rides up above his trousers and the cuffs
shoot out inches beyond the coatsleeves. No dress a
woman ever wore could look that queer unless she put it
on inside out and with her legs through the sleeves. But
up to a few years ago we wore that starched shirt (all the
lovelier in salmon pink) to the office, to the baseball game,
and to clubs or saloons where we sat around laughing at
women's clothes.

We had spring clips three inches long to attach starched
cuffs to sleeves, an ingenuity beyond women's logic. And
the starched collar hung on long after the cuff had dis-
appeared. Modernity achieved the climax of a collar that
was folded and so had a duller edge than the fully respectable knife blade, and there we stuck for a quarter of

a century. Unstable people, men with no standing in the community — little better than bohemians or vagabonds, really — began to experiment with unstarched collars. The pillars of society countered with something called a "semisoft" that was supposed to allow you to remain respected while feeling comfortable. But the fully male, or financial, mind stuck to starch and a good credit rating. The model that Mr. Herbert Hoover was still wearing in 1932 was called a Belmont (giving names to, say, women's perfumes was absurd) and he appears to have a lot of Belmonts left. Millions of other men still have them, but they are slowly becoming specialized. When you see one now the best guess is that the wearer is a banker or is on his way to church.

The suit in that snapshot is made of material approximately as heavy as horse blanketing; evening clothes still are. Every step in its modification amounted to a revolution, with the government in peril. The chest and lapels had to be stiffened with horsehairs, which worked their way out so that sometimes you could not tell whether it was your coat or your Belmont that was sawing at your neck. Moreover, natural law, the law that holds the stars in their courses, required the coat to have four buttons. Law and order hung on the fourth button; a three-button coat symbolized anarchy and the assassination of President McKinley. That opinion still holds in banks and bond houses, at least on the Atlantic seaboard. A customer's man can wear a three-button coat, provided the rest of his dress is seemly and he does not associate with Communists. But anyone who handles actual money or has access to the books must post a bond and add another button.

If it took generations to evolve lightweight underwear, it took even longer to adjust suitings to temperature. One of history's greatest revolutionists was probably a book-keeper. To protect his suit from ink he kept a (black) alpaca or seersucker jacket at the office. One midsummer day he forgot to change it for his black broadcloth horse blanket when he went out to lunch. Within a decade many men were wearing alpaca or seersucker or mohair suits in hot weather and it hardly took a quarter-century to make "sports wear" acceptable. ("Sports" is a virile word but "summer suit" would be too much like "summer dress.") But there is a point beyond which the stabilizers of society will not go: so long as you are in the office you have got to have something over your shirt. A newspaper-man wears a vest but no jacket, a bank teller wears a jacket but no vest.

By 1900 what we called pepper-and-salt gray was as acceptable as black anywhere except at church or in a bank, and a few years later the blue serge suit was here to stay, presumably forever. It was then so radical an innovation that it threatened to overturn society, but now it is man's best insurance against social unrest. He would feel safe in it even at a female fashion show. Once the wall was breached, it was reasonably easy for other colors and mixed patterns to come in. But in spite of *Esquire* we are not likely to imitate the birds and become the colorful sex — we are not going to blossom in yellows, bright greens, electric blues and awning stripes. And —

here I am afraid I've got to play on my own team for a while — it will be just as well if women don't undertake to design clothes for men. I grant the correctness of the urge: it's hard to look at any male outfit and keep a straight face. But when Elizabeth Hawes, for instance, set out to improve on it, she did far worse. The main reason is simple; it is the same reason that keeps most women from wearing the all but nonexistent bathing suits that a few women can wear successfully: we haven't got the figures. The kindest thing anyone can do for the male body is to cover it up.

Women dress in docile subjection to the advertising agencies but men dress logically and for the sake of establishing their masculinity and dignity — and dignity is always heading toward the First National Bank. At a time when women wore removable jabots which could be fitted to their blouses with hooks and eyes, men were wearing white facings on their vests. They were called vestees and they were fastened to the under side with little safety pins. But no element of fashion entered here; anyone who saw vestees knew that the wearer was solvent. It wasn't fashion that had us spreading out our ties to fill the full V of our vests and pinning them in place, then shifting to narrow knitted ties. It is not fashion that litters a man's bureau with ties discarded because no one is wearing that kind any more. Ties are geared to the stock market and a decent regard for the opinion of one's fellow men. A couple of years ago women were wearing platform shoes that made them look clubfooted. It was an ugly, idiotic fashion, one that the shoe business could never have put over on men. You may recently have seen in store windows men's shoes with three- and four-inch soles of deeply corrugated crêpe rubber. They have a logical purpose; if it happens to be raining the wearer will not get his feet wet.

Besides, they are virile — they weigh so much it takes strength to wear them. And they look rugged, which is to say not only masculine but belligerent. You may have noticed that windbreakers are shorter than they used to be and are tightly belted at the bottom — if the belt has hooks and eyes they are of masculine design. It was not fashion that changed those windbreakers. Manufacturers modeled them on combat jackets. Soldiers, I have pointed out, are not effeminate.

But soldiers — and sailors — went almost too far in making that clear, during the war. If fashions change rapidly, they always come back again. The wife I began by quoting (my wife, I admit) was dead sure that women will never again commit the absurdity of knee-length formal evening dresses. I am dead sure they will, and before long now. The dresses will have a new name, there will be some new way of designating them, but they will be worn to formal gatherings and they will end at the knee. I saw the corset disappear forever. Women had come into a glorious liberation. They would never again submit to the slavery that had given them tuberculosis, kept them off the tennis court and subjected them to fainting spells. It isn't a corset now, it's a girdle even when it comes close to the chin, and it hasn't got whalebone or steel stays in it but only a two-way stretch.

Women would never go back to the corset, but here it is. Which is why our young military men threw a scare into me.

All of a sudden they began to raise beards. You saw sideburns, burnsides, goatees, Vandykes, wreath beards, chin beards, shovel beards and up to forty other styles that had been classified and illustrated in manuals for barbers during the presidency of Ulysses S. Grant. That era must be called the Dark Age of American life. I have suggested that the American male is not remarkable for good looks and it is an open question how bright he is, but for a generation and a half he had been bright enough not to deliberately look his worst. But here he was growing hair on his face as if he were his own grandfather. For a couple of years it seemed as if our young men were going to bring us peace and the comic-strip face in a dead heat. As it turned out, they didn't; by the end of the first year of peace the beard was gone.

But it is gone for only a little while; it is certain to start back again and this time it will make the grade. We will all look as much as nature permits like Civil War generals and House of David baseball players. We will be tucking beards under our vestees; we will be carrying tweezers and pocket brushes to keep them neat. There will be a seller's market in mustache cups, hair tonics and barber's wax. The rest of the culture-complex may ride in with the beard: black broadcloth suits, baggy drawers, boiled shirts, Belmont collars, high-laced shoes and sleeve garters.

It is a dead-sure thing. Men never succumb to fashion

but they do act on conclusions they have reached by severely analytical logic. And beards are indicated by logic in which no one can find a flaw and of a kind that has always been binding. At first glance, anyway, a beard is not effeminate.

10

Anyone Can Talk to a Genius

THE WORLD is full of people who practice the arts. You may run into one of them, or a half dozen, when you drop in at a friend's house or go out to dinner, tea or a cocktail party. As a class, they are agreeable, amusing and even delightful people; but the chances are you have frequently wondered why one or another of them ruined what had promised to be a pleasant evening.

Practically all such social friction is avoidable. Why hasn't an etiquette writer composed a manual of conduct in the company of artists? It need be only a pamphlet, with nothing in it more difficult than the directions that tell a Boy Scout what to do when he gets lost in the woods. All you require, really, are some simple principles and a little practice at sizing up the course, so that your tee shot will be right. Remember the anecdote that has worked through all the arts but seems to have been permanently fastened on a celebrated orchestra conductor.

After half an hour of enthusiastic, but of course objective, explanation of his talent, he checks himself and says, "But, my dear friend, let us talk about you. Tell me, what did you think of my interpretation of the Bloch concerto?"

Writers are the commonest risk, because there are more of them; so let's begin with them. Mark Twain said, "There are three infallible ways of pleasing an author, and the three form a rising scale of compliment: 1, To tell him you have read one of his books; 2, To tell him you have read all of his books; 3, To ask him to let you read the manuscript of his forthcoming book. No. 1 admits you to his respect; No. 2 admits you to his admiration; No. 3 carries you clear to his heart."

I'm sorry, but this is false gospel and full of danger. It is never wrong to tell a writer that you like (correction: admire) his stuff — provided you have read some of it. But never take the chance if you haven't. You say, with decent moderation, that you couldn't put his new novel down till you had finished it, you wished it never would end. Fine so far. A glow has lighted up in him, and he has recognized you as the rare reader whose subtlety of understanding makes a novelist's hard and dreary toil worth while. So he says, "Did you think that the outcome of the love affair was unbearably grim?" Or, "The ape who reviewed it for the *Times* missed the whole point of Roger's death. Did you have any trouble understanding what I was doing?" There is no way out. Ten seconds later you are the kind of dull-witted Philistine who makes the artist's life a long agony.

As for asking to see an unfinished manuscript — with

nine writers out of ten, never. It is good practice to ask, "What are you working on now?" That merely shows you have an intelligent interest in the health of American literature, and he can say, "A novel," in perfect safety. But you must never ask, "What about?" True, if he happens to be the one out of ten, he may indeed beam at you, take you by the hand, and lead you straight to the manuscript, and thereafter telephone you daily to keep you in touch with the unfolding miracle — and it will serve you right. All writers at work have professional anxieties stewing and fermenting in them; they are walking down an empty road at night, with a new moon over their left shoulder, and something ghastly just inside the woods is about to scream. The other nine have, as well as this anxiety, a conviction that it is desperately dangerous to talk about a book before it is finished. You have brought the book into peril merely by mentioning it, and though the writer may have some magic incantation that will neutralize the jinx, if you press him any farther, all will be lost. He can get across the room from you and make the magical signs that avert the evil eye; but he has some remnant awareness that that would be discourteous.

But plenty of openings are available to you, gambits that will assure you a pleasant evening and the novelist's profound respect. Begin with an amused jeer at a review that spoke unfavorably of his latest novel — he will remember it, all right. Or, and this is better, allude negligently (if you prefer, with astonishment) to the understanding of women that his female characters demonstrate. It is useful to know that there is one infallible approach. I leave the exact phrasing to your sense of style, but the burden of what you say is, "Why did the publishers stop advertising your book so soon?" Your awareness that his publishers bungled their great opportunity will carry you "clear into his heart." He has met a kindred and understanding soul; you need feel no further responsibility for the conversation and no fear of an unsuccessful evening.

With writers, you see, there may be difficulties or complexities. None is possible with actors, provided you understand that an actor is quite willing to be told how good he is. You don't even have to like the play he is in. In fact, if he is triumphing over the handicap of a dreary play or clumsy lines, so much the better. Even a ham can look good in a good vehicle, but it takes an artist to bring out what a bad script tried to do but failed. You may not need more than the word "nuance" — don't waste it on his voice, for everybody knows how versatile that is. The just perceptible tremor of his lips, the finger that is half raised and then falls so helplessly, the body slumping with despair for a second before it straightens into heroic resolution — mention one of these, and your drive will go three hundred yards straight down the middle of the fairway. It takes genuine perceptiveness to understand how fine these bits are, whereas anyone can appreciate a big scene or an all-out speech. He is happy to meet a person for whom the art of acting exists. And a happy actor makes a good companion.

Certain other perceptions are more rewarding, but require more skill. If you know, for example, that he is carrying the actress who plays opposite him, splendid. Every actor is certain that one of his finest gifts is his ability to compensate for the mistakes or inadequacy of another actor, and "You certainly hold Harriet's head out of the water in the quarrel scene" is first-rate conversation. But reconnoiter the ground; Harriet may be heading for Reno when the play's run ends, so that she can marry him.

This brings up a matter you may run into with any artist. We can get at it with a story Cordell Hull's colleagues used to tell about him, when he was in the Senate and had a reputation for playing his cards close to his chest. One Senator made a bet at long odds that he could find a topic on which he could get a forthright commitment from Mr. Hull. While the others stood by, he went to Mr. Hull in the cloakroom and asked him what time it was. Mr. Hull took out his watch, gazed at it contemplatively, put it back in his pocket, and said to the inquirer, "What time does *your* watch say?" When an artist asks you what you think of another artist, don't wade right in; ask him what *his* watch says.

For you never can tell. Novelists are probably the least predictable. Some of them genuinely admire the work of others and are willing to have you like it out loud. But don't run reckless chances. If the author you are talking to writes light social satire, it is probably safe to admire a novel of thick gloom about the miserable clay eaters in the piney-woods country. But watch out. If the poor-white tragedy is outselling the light comedy, you haven't read it. You aren't safe in merely disliking it, you haven't even heard of it.

On the whole, it is safest to like someone else's work when you talk to a painter. I don't know whether painters have earthquakeproof egos or whether they are less subject to envy or jealousy; but they can often see a lot of merit in one another's work. And that isn't all: a painter is likely to talk better about another's work than about his own.

Poets are at the other extreme, and there is only one living poet, or there had *better* be only one. That is flat, the only absolute I can give you. There are no exceptions. Also, it is retroactive for thirty years: there has been no other poet for a generation, not even a bad one. Not to have read any other will not do. To refrain from mentioning any other will not do, either, and it makes trouble if you mention one for the sole purpose of saying he is poor. It is wrong for you to have read him at all.

Dancers may chatter a lot sometimes, but they are inarticulate. They communicate, as they will tell you, kinesthetically. You will usually understand what one means when she makes a sinuous motion with her hand, revolves a foot in a circle, or begins a sentence with a word, continues it by thrusting a hip four inches out of line, and ends it by going into a crouch that would become a leap if she were not sitting in a chair. But you will not understand what her vocabulary means; she doesn't understand it, either, till her muscles have explained to her. You can collect a few pat terms like "tension," "dynamics," "space line," "inner dance," which will show that you are a person of good will and know beauty when someone expresses it for you. But don't suppose the words mean what they do in other contexts; don't assume they mean anything. Wait for the rotating wrist to tell you.

There is a hazard: you must immediately get it clearly in mind what kind of dancing the girl does. You know all about such things as tap dancing and clog dancing; but don't mention them. Don't use the word "dancing," either. To her it means ballroom dancing, instructing at a dance hall, or at best being in the chorus of a musical show. Three other words you must accurately understand. "Ballet" is old-fashioned, inexpressive and reactionary. "The dance" means the sort of thing you are just about catching up with; but most likely the girl you are talking to has got a long way beyond it and is unhappy when you use the term. To her it means a program note that says, approximately, "This is a dance of the soul frustrated by an industrial society," and barefoot girls running round in circles with their heads thrown back — frightfully old stuff. She feels about "the dance" the way you feel about red-flannel underwear or bags of asafetida for colds. In no art did more ever hang on a single word — the definite article. She cannot get along with you unless you are in the know, and to be in the know you must always say "dance." You also need the verb "express." Ask her what dance expresses, what she is expressing, what the numbers she is working up express. Even so, as I have said, unless she can get out on the floor, where she can make herself understood, the conversation may be a little like one conducted with a somnambulist. What do you care? She is a pretty child, and it is a pleasure to watch her express.

The breed most likely to cross you up is the musicians. Never let a sense of well-being get such a hold on you at a party that you go to a recital or a symphony with the musician who has been talking so amusingly. When you get there, you hear music; but what your companion hears is something wrong in the second row of first violins. If not that, the oboes made their entrance on the wrong beat, or the conductor's delusion that he understands Sibelius should have shock treatment at the nearest sanitarium. Don't misunderstand this. He is enjoying the music and is only sorry that it isn't being played better; he isn't aware that he is making you loathe it.

The key to successful conversation here is that you cannot bluff. Of course, you will never meet a musician who isn't superb, but let it go at that; don't tell one why, how and wherein he is good unless you know. As a matter of fact, unless you know what you are talking about, don't talk about music; let him do the talking. You won't have any trouble getting him started: just pause for a moment.

We must separate the singers, and then separate the women on the highest eminence, opera and concert stars, though there are so few of them and they breathe such rarefied air that the likes of us are not apt to encounter them. There is no problem about talking to them or listening to them except that your knees may get tired. I saw it printed somewhere that there was once a soprano who admired another soprano; but the statement is a lie. There has never been a contralto who did, either.

The general run of singers, male and female, are usually agreeable, but they are without the ability of other musicians to talk fluently about anything.

Musicians as a class, however, are lighthearted, gay

and have a good time. Their great comfort for a hostess and her guests is that an incautious word is not likely to throw them into the sulks, their egos are not susceptible to wounds, and they do not walk down dark roads at midnight on their guard against the hex. We may say that they have a low flash point and are a bit hard to follow. But this last is our fault, not theirs, for their logic is always crystal clear. If a musician goes to the corner to mail a letter, it may surprise you or me when he calls a cab and takes a train to Scarsdale; but that exhibits not his irrationality but the slowness of our reactions. On the way to the corner he happened to think that he had never been to Scarsdale, or he wondered how long the train ride was. Why should he remain ignorant any longer, or why should he not settle the doubt? The logic is clear, the reasoning unanswerable. Likewise with musicians' conversation; it follows the same pattern, its logic is flawless, and if you cannot find the key to it, whose fault is that? Social occasions heighten the normal buoyancy of musicians, and for my money they are insurance against dullness, present fewer hazards than any other artists and are the best companions.

One caution. All authorities agree that it is thoughtless to ask a musician to play at a party. But this carries a postscript: it is also unnecessary.

11

Pocket Guide to Horse Opera

HORSE OPERA — Hollywood's finest art form — is an inexhaustible source of wonder and delight to those of us who love it; but it is easy to miss its subtlest beauties unless a few principles are understood. Some people think the Western movie and the horse opera are different forms. Those people are wrong. They have been misled by variations the script writer is free to choose among, just as a cook is free to use either butter or vegetable shortening in a cake. Westerns and horse operas are the same thing, and just as all cakes have flour in them, they have five basic ingredients. There must be horses, there must be at least one cowboy, the hero must get into at least one fistfight, somebody must be chasing somebody else, and at short intervals everybody except the girl must shoot Frontier-model Colt revolvers. The girl can shoot one, too, but that's optional; she doesn't have to.

If she does, it's because she's in a mood of pique at the

hero and is simply substituting gunfire for dialogue. It would be out of character for her to hit him or anyone else. You must understand that shooting is not necessarily hostile. A few shots exchanged by strangers often serve as an introduction and may lead to a beautiful friendship. And gunfire can clear up a misunderstanding, or relieve the hero's embarrassment, or express the villain's frustration. When it is hostile, you can tell which is our side by the range it's done at. If somebody crouching by the Last Chance Saloon two blocks away gets winged, we did the shooting; the others would miss at farther than one. Finally, nobody has to load his gun; a Frontier six-shooter holds more cartridges than a machine gun. At the end of ten minutes you may be worried lest our side get jumped while reloading, but that is for suspense. It has never happened yet.

Those are the necessities. The optional ingredients make up the artist's palette, the embroiderer's silks. Of course there are steers, the Thundering Herd; they are very common but by no means required. Then there are burros, pack mules, bull teams (oxen pulling freight wagons and driven by bullwhackers, who crack whips), wild horses (broomtails), vicious horses (for the top hand) and sheep (sheepherders are never our side). There can be trappers, miners (or prospectors, who are old), emigrants (with covered wagons), stage drivers, postmasters, Pony Express riders, scouts (who are second leads), sheriffs or marshals, nesters (farmers, either humble or sinister), Indian traders (vile), the U.S. Cavalry and Indians. Indians are Apaches, who wear a single feather in their hair, or Sioux, who wear war bonnets. There may be saloons (not often for drinking; they are where the dance hall girls are and where the fistfight occurs), stage-coaches, ranch houses, the waterhole, placer mines ("Oh! Susanna" in the background music), deserts and mountains, and the open range.

Horse opera imposes on itself a severe and very intricate protocol. Thus, outlaws are not necessarily badmen, though they may be, and neither badmen nor outlaws are necessarily villains — they may be our side. (Texans are always our side and always Supermen in hair pants.) A sheriff or a marshal may be a villain, and a deputy nearly always is; but an officer of the U.S. Cavalry can't be. Occasionally he can be a coward. Any Army officer who is a spy is the hero. Neither our side nor the Cavalry can shoot at a wagon train; anybody else can. Everybody can always chase anybody else and in fact must, up to four chases going on at once, except that the Cavalry can chase only Indians. (En masse, that is; a single Cavalry-man can do anything, particularly when wounded.) Indians are as you will; they can be heroes, villains, outlaws, badmen, our side, or strictly on their own. If a cowboy is a villain, there must be at least one more cowboy, and he is the second lead if not the hero. Cowboys outrank everyone else, even General Custer. If a trick is to be taken, they are the ace that takes it.

Horse opera is so vigorous it always dominates when Hollywood tries to mix it with another standard movie type. Thus several recent films undertook to blend horse opera with the Civil War motif, which you might think would result in curdling. Not at all. The basic ingredients again proved that they are what counts, and all you could notice was an occasional conflict in conventions. The latest of these mixtures I have seen was called *The Redhead and the Cowboy*, a title that would enable any connoisseur to take it from there. There was only one cowboy. There was only one Indian, and he was not called on to do any Indian stuff. There was an Indian trader, which meant that here was the villain, and since he was also a military spy, there had to be a noble spy, too. The noble spy masqueraded as a cattle buyer, and that is as close as the film came to steers, though in one sequence there were sounds of cattle offstage. There was one dance hall girl, heroine type; there was gold, but you saw neither it nor the mine; there were covered wagons, and they got shot up during a chase, but that sequence did not last two minutes. The cowboy was whittled down to basic cowboy functions; he fell for the girl, he rode a horse, he had a fistfight, he kept on shooting, he captured the villain.

All this was pure horse opera; the Civil War motif stayed strictly inside it, and there were only two problems. In order to bring out the Civil War angle, while keeping the horse opera aspect, the scene had to be West Texas, Arizona, or New Mexico. The producers settled for New Mexico, and simply told the location department to find some mesas. (Just south of Carson City, Nevada, I think.)

But the harder problem was to observe the protocol of Civil War movies. Hollywood long ago decided that though the North won the war, the Southern belle won the North; and that if there was a Southern villain, he had to be balanced by a Northern one. *The Redhead and the*

Cowboy balanced him with a whole countryside of Northern villains, who were cruel even to horses. The cowboy was neither Northern nor Southern but just for the girl; the girl was a spy as well as a belle; so the secondary hero, Northern, was a spy, too. But how could a Southerner, even though a villain, be dishonorable? This one was going to steal the Northern gold (which was in the wagon train), and that was the whole point. Easy enough — he could be dishonorable if the South did not profit from his baseness. So this was the last few weeks of the war, when it was too late to save the Cause, and though the villain would pretend to capture the gold as a patriotic Confederate, he would basely keep it for himself. That being decided, the cowboy and the secondary hero and some badmen chased the girl. The sheriff and the secondary hero and the badmen chased the cowboy. The badmen and the secondary hero chased each other by turns. The badmen put on Confederate uniforms, and chased the wagon train (permissible, since they were not *real* Cavalry). Everybody but the girl shot at everybody else, including the girl, and she got knocked down twice. It was not only horse opera, it was a vintage year.

The scene of horse opera is the Old West. This is Nature's never-never land, all poetry, fantasy, wonder. Take the Long Trail, which stretches five or six hundred miles from Texas to Dodge City (where Boot Hill is). They drive big herds up it to the railroad, fighting Indians and cattle rustlers; they sing all night to keep the critters from stampeding, but they get away once and trample at least one of our side. A map won't show you mountains within four hundred miles westward from the Long Trail; but all the months they drive those steers north, the high ridge of California's Sierra is always in the background. In the foreground are two rounded hills — buttes, not mesas. Day by day, month by month, spring to fall, the steers plod on, the hero goes without shaving, the villain poisons the girl's mind, and we are always passing those same two buttes.

They are versatile buttes. The Santa Fé Trail is where the Indians or the outlaws chase the stagecoach, with the cowboy or the U.S. Cavalry closing in on them maybe in time, and the blurred shapes back of the careening coach are those two buttes. The Oregon Trail is what the emigrants travel in their white-tops, and all the way to Oregon, through the dust from the wheels and the smoke of gunfire, we keep catching glimpses of those same buttes.

The same with the river. It has banks for the herd to slither down and the white-tops to lurch up. It has a ford for the chase to gallop through. It has a bend for boats to come round and the Indians to lurk behind. It is Powder River (where they let 'er buck), the Platte (a mile wide, stranger, an inch deep, and she runs uphill), the Willamette (trail's end at last, thank heaven), the American (that's gold, podner), and the wide Missouri (I'm bound away, across). It is an all-purpose river, the same width, the same depth, and the same current everywhere, the two buttes and beyond them the Sierra. Those trees on the far side of the river would be eucalyptus anywhere but in the Old West; here they are cottonwoods, symbolic cottonwoods.

You must understand about horses, too. If they are walking, the cowboy is going to be ambushed (dry-gulched, we say) or this will be a love scene. Otherwise, horses gallop. Nothing must happen except at a dead run, and a horse-opera horse can gallop all day or all night or both. A mountainside is there to be galloped down, without sliding pads. A horse may buck, but it may not throw anyone on our side except Bob Hope. A villain may be shot from the saddle, but no one on our side can ever suffer such indignity. The cowboy can leap into the saddle from a second-story window, but the girl can't, for she is refined. Our side's horses may appear to be dying of thirst a desperate distance from the waterhole, but they get there. They have to, for an earlier shot has shown the badmen taking cover there under the trees to dry-gulch us. (I forgot to say that the waterhole is the place where it's all right to do the shooting with a rifle.) Horses do not get screen credit except in musicals — in what, loathing them, we may call horse operettas.

That does it, except for some small items. Don't be taken in by the ragged jeans the girl wears in the early shots; remember she is refined. She has a dress, and though Bette Davis can get her dress dirty, our girl can't. All one day in a stagecoach chased by Indians, all the next day in the saddle, that night crawling under a table when the fight starts at the Last Chance Saloon — no matter, the dress is still immaculate. Also the canvas covers of the emigrant wagons: spotless white when we reach the Willamette. And watch out for an optical illusion. You might take those underslung steers for whitefaces — that is, Herefords — but they aren't. Them's longhorns, stranger.

In Hollywood's less stylized forms, you have often

wondered why Bette Davis or Barbara Stanwyck or Joan Fontaine was behaving in that curious way. (The script writer wondered, too.) Horse opera knows no such obscurity. The cowboy is going to save the girl, so he can be shot at, so he can be chased, so he can chase the villain, who is chasing the girl, so he can shoot back, so the girl can save him.

Use the quirt, and if that won't do it, shoot faster.

12

Homicide in the Home

EVERYBODY reads detective stories, but publishers will tell
you that nowhere near enough people buy them. In the
twenty-five-cent reprints, of course, they sell by the multiple million, far outdistancing the other two staples of
light fiction, Western stories and the odds-bodkins species
of historical novel. But the mystery fan refuses to pay two
dollars and a half for the gore he revels in, and most of
the circulation of most mysteries is by lending library.

Lending libraries, in fact, are the only certain market.
It is an automatic market; a publisher can count on selling
to it, with little effort on his part, from twenty-five hundred to four thousand copies of nearly any mystery he
brings out. (That he can count on it is one reason so
many mysteries are dreadfully bad. Another fact is that
from such a sale the author will get no more than twelve
hundred dollars at the utmost — wretched pay, considering how long the writing of any book requires — and so is

under pressure to turn them out as fast as possible.) A sale of between ten and fifteen thousand copies appears to be the maximum that well-known practitioners of the trade can hope for. A handful of writers do regularly exceed it and sell impressive numbers of their books, many of which have already made them much more money as magazine serials; but very few, perhaps only one in ten years, ever appear on the list of best-sellers. Eight cents a day at the lending library or a quarter at the newsstand — that appears to be the public's idea of what it should pay for the fiction it most enjoys.

Apart from the occasional readers of mysteries — which is virtually everybody — we can distinguish two kinds of genuine fan. One is the addict, and there are many. Few days pass when he isn't reading a mystery; in the course of a year he may get through two hundred, three hundred, sometimes even more. He never passes the corner drugstore without wistfully scrutinizing the reprint shelves to see if by some happy fortune they hold one he has missed. The other fan is like the periodic drinker. (You may so classify me.) He abstains for a time, feeling no craving. Then suddenly he has to go on a bender and will read a dozen in succession, or as many more as may be required to satisfy his very curious and involved need.

I use such words as "addict" and "bender" deliberately, for an odd thing about this form of light literature is that its devotees feel shamefaced about liking it. They act, at least they talk, as if the liking were reprehensible, or evidence of crude taste or of a defect in character. This sheepishness, I feel sure, is a form of literary snobbery, and I deplore it. These people want you to understand that they know what serious fiction is and respect it a great deal, and know, too, that mysteries are mere "escape literature." They certainly are, though that is by no means the full truth about them.

And, besides, there is an additional awkward fact: all fiction is escape literature. One reason any novel is read is that it takes the reader out of the actual world and suspends the demands reality lays on him. That is true no matter how realistically it may deal with human experience or how earnestly it may prepare us to deal with our own experience. In the respect that release from actuality is one of the boons a reader seeks, there is no difference between Proust's *Remembrance of Things Past* and any trumpery item called, say, *Murder Falls Downstairs.* (If that title has not appeared yet, it will tomorrow.)

How can we explain this intense interest of so many people? On the surface it is illogical, even unnatural. Murder is the absolute prerequisite of the type. Though there are other grave and terrible crimes — robbery, kidnaping, rape, for instance — the detective story usually ignores them unless it can make use of them on the way to murder. And after all, murder is the sin of Cain — the act that mankind has always considered the most abhorrent, the one that removes the perpetrator from human sympathy and requires his own life to be forfeited in return. It is the essence of unrighteousness, anarchy and violence, and most stories about it involve further violence, perhaps torture, and such undesirable emotions as fear, terror, horror, grief and despair. Yet the reader not only tolerates them; he demands them and converts them into pleasure.

The demand is so imperative that in default of good mysteries, bad ones will do, even very bad ones. The lowest level of detective stories is more naïve and inept than the corresponding level of any other kind of popular fiction. The most trivial hammock novel has to have some modicum of professional skill or it will die on the market; but mysteries can be childish in conception, crude in construction, and half-literate in style — and still be read.

Good ones, of course, are a product of expert professional skill. Their characters, though needed only in relation to the specialized theme of murder, have such attributes as characters must have in any adult fiction — genuine liveliness, recognizable motives, authentic emotions, plausible behavior. Their structure has more firmness and functional strength than most kinds of novel require. Their style is at least workmanlike, and in the top bracket considerably more than that. People of such excellence as Carter Dickson and Dorothy Sayers in England, or Rex Stout and Raymond Chandler here, write first-rate prose — precise, apt, fastidious, pleasing, versatile. Sometimes more than that may be said. Literary critics of impressive solemnity have argued that Dashiell Hammett's prose is an artistic instrument fully as original and as subtle as Ernest Hemingway's.

One reason for the popularity of detective stories is obvious. You can be sure in advance that you are going to read a story — and this is one of the few remaining departments of fiction where you can be sure. Throughout this century, fiction has greatly widened the range of its interests, with the result that it may be about anything on earth and is likely to contain material that used to be confined to textbooks. It may include something like a treatise on politics, sociology, world peace, the smelting of iron ore, or, especially, psychology. For the commonest stage setting in fiction is now the inside of a character's mind, and the commonest effort of novelists is to explore the subtle gradations of the characters' feelings and motives.

This is fine and has enriched the art of fiction; but much of it has come at the expense of story. Yet story is the root of fiction, perhaps the most primitive element but also the eternal one. It is good to learn about economics and good to follow the deep secrecies of personality; but doing so will not feed our hunger to know what happened. The *what* rather than the *why* — what began this? what happened next? what did it lead to? what was the outcome? Nothing will ever end our desire to have those questions answered; but much fiction now disregards them. This is why every so often even sophisticated readers stampede by the hundred thousand to read, say, *Gone With the Wind,* in which something is always happening and happening fast. And why, in fact, a reader picks up a detective story.

For, however inept it may be, if it were not a story, it would not have been published. Something of primary importance, a murder, will happen, and this will set in motion a chain of events, which will move with great speed to a climax. People will be caught up in those events and will be unable to get away from them. A fundamental question will be asked; there will be a conflict of powerful forces; there will be hazard and danger and suspense, flight and pursuit, the ebb and flow of fortune; and in the end the question will be answered. Such fiction may be trivial, but the elements that compose it are from the core of all fiction.

Moreover, there will be a puzzle for the reader to solve. In a way, all novels are mystery stories, for they try to solve the puzzle of human personality; but this is a formally constructed puzzle. Who committed the murder and why? The fundamental division between kinds is to be made right here. In one kind, everything else is subordinated to the perfection of the puzzle, and there are readers who prefer this to all others. Something like a code of fair practices is taken for granted. The writer will make the puzzle entirely logical; he will permit neither weak links nor implausibilities. He will withhold from the reader nothing that is essential to the solution, and when he solves it, will use nothing the reader has not seen. He will rule out chance, coincidence, and the accidental — everything that happens will be the result of something that has happened before. All this being attended to, he will then do everything at his command to deceive the reader, who in turn will get his pleasure from attempting to penetrate the deception.

The other kind, of both stories and readers, is larger. Here the puzzle need not be quite so tight or the job of solving it so rigorous and involved, and other values count more. The reader is not concerned with solving the puzzle so much as with seeing it solved, and his pleasure is derived primarily from the excitement of the story.

There are many sorts of mystery, and readers have many tastes. But I think that few of us genuine fans like the frivolous mystery. We accept with complete equanimity the idea of death by violence — though writers take care to murder unsympathetic people and to murder them before we can get interested in them as individuals — but we do not regard it as a joke. Lightness of touch in the writing, yes, and let the characters have as much humor as you like. Indeed, gaiety may intensify fear, and wit or humor may be an effective background for horror. But the deed of Cain is no laughing matter, and we want no merry wisecrackers romping through the mystery in a spirit of good clean fun. Or unclean fun, either.

To some degree, many of us also resent the contamination of the detective story by the love story, which apparently is sure to be blended with it from now on. Perhaps it can be kept from diminishing the effect, though that is difficult; but it is almost certain to distract us sometimes from the central interest. Love in the shadow of death is much too big a theme for the detective story to handle — this is, after all, literature of entertainment — and incidental romance is likely to seem unimportant. Besides, the detective is usually a party to the romance, and we want to meet him again in later books, where he can hardly be provided with a succession of new girls.

What we have come to call the hard-boiled mystery was a valuable development, which has left a permanent impression on the form; but it soon became a fashion and now tends to degenerate into a mere formula — in a field that runs to formula too often for its own good. It was a necessary corrective, a much needed realism. Talented writers, as Mr. Raymond Chandler has said, were beginning to persuade us that fictional murder was something appropriate to vicarages and garden parties and that mystery itself hinged on whether the curate liked lemon or milk in his tea.

Such books as Mr. Hammett's and those of Mr. Chandler himself centered on the brutality, cruelty, shock and inhumanity we were in some danger of glossing over — and in doing so invigorated the art and sharpened the reader's pleasure. Yet for all their emphasis on realism of detail, the hard-boiled stories remain essentially romantic (it is difficult to see how stories of murder could be anything else without introducing a solemnity we do not want), and they tend to cross the line into another form. They tend, that is, to become stories of psychological anarchy — pure horror — which is a fascinating thing, perhaps a deeper one, but is certainly not mystery and its solution.

Good writers are always imitated, but such writers as Mr. Hammett and Mr. Chandler are hard to imitate well. The result has been a swarm of lesser writers, who know the words but cannot sing the tune, who do not understand the difficult form they are imitating. They have a cheap, inacceptable substitute for talent and for the care that must go into the kind of story they pretend to write — their books are a mechanical repetition of flogging, drinking and sex. The constant obligation of the writer to give his story the appearance of being inevitable, and so to make the parts fit together perfectly, they avoid by pouring another bottle of whisky into the detective or breaking it over his head. This is as frivolous as the curate coquetting with murder in his garden.

Here, I think, we arrive at another basic element in the appeal of detective stories. We think it a flaw if the detective solves the problem by beating the answer out of someone. We demand that he solve it by intelligence. An amusing convention more often than not forbids him to be a policeman (it might be interesting to inquire why we do not want the official police too bright); but he has to have brains, courage, doggedness and ingenuity, and he has to outthink the murderer. The cheaply hardboiled story commits an even worse offense in that sometimes the detective can hardly be distinguished from the thugs who slug him and whom he slugs in turn, and this we deeply resent. He must not be a criminal or use criminal means; he must triumph over criminals. Simply: he is a hero.

Other branches of fiction, faithfully pointing out to us the need of understanding what life is like, deal sympathetically with all kinds of people, many of them far from admirable. Doubtless this makes for human charity, but also it confuses moral values. One of the functions of literature has always been to tell us what to admire — what a hero is. To put it as crudely as possible, we are to admire heroes and hate villains: we are to believe that life makes sense morally. Every detective story, by dramatizing retribution before our eyes, says in a loud voice that life does make that sense. A sophisticated reader may not like being told that part of his pleasure in a Nero Wolfe novel comes from seeing virtue triumph over vice, as assuredly it does not always do in more serious fiction. But that is true nevertheless. The foundation of every novel is a simple fable, and the fable that underlies all detective stories is the same. Justice and righteousness triumph, and the hero, the good man, proves that the decency of mankind is unconquerable. We may not consciously acknowledge it, but that is one reason we read detective stories. This reason can be but a slight part of anyone's motives in reading them, but it goes deep.

Another equally slight part goes even deeper. Is the most avid fan likely to be a person of absolute probity, living with the utmost quietness and respectability? Possibly, and if so, the release he seeks may be found in an imaginary world of violent feelings and actions. Yet if that were the essential, the sheer adventure novel would serve him just as well. Why should he, then, insist on the thing that is absolutely tabooed, the true deed of darkness?

It is said with some plausibility that the mystery story gives us a chance to gratify our secret and primitive wish to kill somebody. A nagging wife or husband, an angry boss, anyone we think has injured us will set up a tension in the primitive part of us. He must pay for it, we feel, and since we have no way of safely making him pay, the injustice festers. And so, this theory holds, we get relief in the symbols the detective story provides. The corpse in the story is a person who has injured us, perhaps all those who have ever injured us rolled into one, and in the mild daydream printed in a book we find a safe expression of our wish. Symbolically we have got our revenge.

So the primitive part of the personality responds to the story, and the word "safety" is the key. We cannot contemplate the actual fact of murder. The idea of it is too terrible to be borne. Yet it exerts a powerful fascination. The taboo is fascinating in itself. And however sane our life may be, we are always aware that there is great evil in the world and there are a thousand threats of danger. Put the evil and the dangers into a fantasy printed in a book, however, and revulsion, terror, horror become harmless; in our own safe living room we can find enjoyment in evils from which we would flee panic-stricken if we met them in actuality. And not only enjoy them but triumph over them.

That, I think, is not the principal reason we read the story, it is not even an important reason; but surely it is always there.

If we examine the simplest human action, we can always find an intricate tangle of motives underlying it. One would not want to analyze for very long so satisfying a pleasure as the one an innocent and tangy detective story gives us — this wholesome art, where murder is the natural course of things and there is fun in being scared. And though we might pile up motives all day long, the sum of them would count less than the marvelous fact itself. Here is a quiet house (old and isolated for prefer-

ence), or a dark wood (which few of us ever see nowa-
days), or a sinister city street long after midnight, or a
forlorn figure going to its doom. The moment we read the
words, we know where we are, and in a few pages there
will be a distant, half-strangled scream.

That does it. We are caught by the story, and while we
are reading it, what else matters?

13

The Life and Wife of a Writer

A WRITER is a man who works at home. Also he is a man who can never induce anyone to believe that fact. He has many friends, who treat him indulgently. A striking thing about them is that they are all writers too. Not actual writers, for they can't get time off from office or household affairs, but potential ones. They tell convulsing anecdotes very skillfully, they can mimic people so effectively that you recognize them at once, and they write the most interesting letters — what else has a writer got? They regard him as amiably incompetent at stern, practical things — running an advertising campaign, say, or a committee meeting of the state federation of women's clubs — but they frankly envy him his easy life. He lounges round the house most of the time, doing nothing in particular and doing it on no particular schedule. Be honest now, it's a soft job, isn't it? You spend most of your time loafing, don't you?

A writer's friends have got a lot in common with the public that reads him.

Though amiably incompetent at stern, practical things, I am on the executive committee of an organization that goes clanging off to the fire whenever some violation of civil liberties has occurred locally, or is threatening to occur. My fellow committeemen are doctors, lawyers, college professors, businessmen. And, of course, they are busy. When an emergency arises the organization secretary knows better than to break in on them. She would not interrupt a lawyer who might be dictating a brief, or summon a professor from a lecture, or call on a doctor who was examining someone's wart. But she has it clearly in mind that I haven't got anything to do, so it's my phone that rings.

Let's repeat, writers work at home. If pushed, I will admit that that gives their wives something of a case. But I will tell you what the ideal wife of a writer is and add that she has not been born yet. The ideal wife is one who does not say (indignantly or accusingly or witheringly), "But you weren't doing anything." That is the brightest star in her crown but there are a lot of other stars — will be, I mean, if she is ever born. She does not come into the study to ask if Betty phoned while she was out, if you have got a dollar in change, if it's going to rain this afternoon because which hat shall I wear if it does, if that peculiar noise she heard means that the transmission (which she couldn't distinguish from the fan belt anyway) needs to be looked at. She doesn't come into the study to tell her husband to bring the groceries from the car, have him draw up the petition she is going to circulate for signatures, display the dress she happened to see in a window and what a bargain too, report that the sink is clogged, or say that she has decided we'll have ice cream tonight and he'd better go get it now. Put it simply: she doesn't come into the study. But if she does come in, she never says, "But you weren't doing anything."

(The wives of all the writers I know, let me say right here, are helpmeets, family stabilizers, brighter and pleasanter than their husbands, beautiful, compellingly attractive, dressed with incredible smartness on the pittances allowed them for clothes, the admiration and desire of all the world.) What the non-ideal wife means is that the typewriter wasn't going at the moment. A writer writes, doesn't he? Well, if the typewriter is silent, of course he can't be doing anything important.

When she came into the study with her bright eyes and her eager air, the drone was reading a book. He was dawdling — so why should he swear disgustingly when asked to take the winter coats and hang them on the line? (He was checking something that will make the difference between selling and not selling the piece he is working on, the one that will pay for that marvelous bargain in the window.) Or maybe he wasn't even reading — just sitting at the typewriter with a vacant look in his eyes, practically asleep. His wife has to work hard and so do all her male friends — George, for instance. At this moment George may be telling his secretary what letters to write for him, having his second cocktail with other executives who are conferring about next week's sales convention in Atlantic City, or having a fiendish time making arrangements to take a big buyer to the country club for some golf. George works so hard that he'll have to go fishing for a week right after Atlantic City, and heaven knows she could use a vacation too, but the loafer she's married to was just sitting there.

Listen, sweetheart, I could type this article in about sixty minutes but I can't write it in less than several days. And I don't mean union eight-hour days, either. I'll be working on it during dinner and long after you've gone to sleep exhausted by finding me not typing. While I was sitting there looking dazed I was wondering whether to say that there are moments in a writer's working day when divorce looks like the green pastures and the still waters — whether the editor of *Woman's Day* would get the wrong idea if I put it that way; whether the reader would conclude that I'm a misogynist and a wife-beater. That is, I was working — I was figuring out an effective way of saying what this piece is intended to say. I'd be working on it even if you found me standing on my hands, and I'd be working harder than I am when you hear me typing the words I have finally decided are the right ones. But no writer has ever yet been able to make wife, friends or casual strangers understand that sad but fundamental fact.

Another thing about working at home: it gives you a different slant on one of the most unjustly abused men in history, King Herod. Ogden Nash has a poem about two little girls have we, one at school and one in bed. School is the most beneficent institution that touches a writer's life, and the best schools are the ones that collect the young at eight-fifteen and keep them till half past five. Even those, however, believe that children should have Saturdays and Sundays off — no writer gets either of them off — so that they can play ball under the study windows or have the gang in to listen to some new records just when Pop has begun the big love scene that will make or break the novel. The other child has the radio going all the time he is in bed and doesn't stay in bed very long. He can't go back to school till his temperature has been normal for twenty-four hours, which usually means a week, but he can burst into the study in search of green ink, help with his arithmetic, or a fascinating discussion on what's wrong with the Red Sox. A child's affection is a beautiful thing but one of life's mysteries is why his need to express it reaches maximum just when, after hours of thought so intense that no sensible person would take a job that involved it, you have got the big scene under way at last. Play is creative and the sight of children playing touches your heart but, with the house full of unused typewriter paper, why does creative play require them to make gliders of the manuscript I have just finished?

No writer has ever been able to make the principle clear to wife, child, or George but I'll try once more. If George has just dictated, "Yours of the 28th *ult* received and in reply would say, *re* blurred printing labels on our Tasty Toast — " and someone steps into his office to ask whether he'd like to take the afternoon off and go to the ball game, nothing is lost. George can pick it right up and go on, "it's the printer's fault and the next labels will be all right" — or nod to the stenographer, who will fill it in. But a writer has lost a long, intricate thought sequence and has to go back to the beginning and start over. He has been focusing a skill George has not got on a job George does not have to do — the problem of bringing the right parts of his subject together at just the right place, using exactly the right number of words for that context, and finding exactly the words that will say what he means and will keep the reader from misunderstanding or misinterpreting what they say. That is only a small part of the skill a writer has to use and of the job he is doing with a vacant look in his eye. But it hasn't anything to do with writing interesting letters. A writer could write them too if he could only get a little spare time.

Outside the circle of his family and friends a writer could be accurately described as a man whom the whole world is eager to set right. Don't get me wrong about this. The writer who isn't glad to get a letter saying that someone liked something he has published is simply lying. Furthermore, every writer is glad to have a mistake pointed out if he has actually made one, glad to get and answer letters that take intelligent issue with him, or seriously ask for more evidence, or seriously inquire about anything else related to what he has said. He likes to get intelligent letters, whatever they may be about. Apart from newspaper comment on what he has written, they are his only way of gauging its effect. His mail is an indispensable part of his profession.

But useful letters are only a small part of his mail. To

print anything at all is automatically to press two triggers. One of them sets off a universal need to correct the writer. Grammar, for instance. The world is full of people who learned grammar in the fifth grade and have loved it like a fiancée ever since, without ever realizing that what the books say about it can have but little application to the use writers make of it. By battalions they drop everything else and, at the pitch of an agonized scream, tell the writer he is illiterate. But not only his grammar is wrong: everything else is too. With a holy passion for the truth and a missionary zeal to bring light into the darkness, the battalions shred him paragraph by paragraph, pointing out his errors. Sometimes they are kindly, sometimes angered by his incompetence, sometimes stricken with despair for the future of a race that permits obviously half-witted men to provide its reading matter.

Now those errors have a striking singularity: they are seldom there. You can take issue with a writer's opinions, interpretations, logic, or conclusions, but be advised to think twice before you question his facts. He got there before you did, he dug out the facts at the sources, and he checked them thoroughly before he published them. That is his job and the plain truth is that the accuracy of American writing is awesomely high: the chances are thousands to one that what any reader takes to be a misstatement isn't one. Inconsiderate mistakes are, alas, sometimes unavoidable (remember that they may be the copy editor's or the proofreader's instead of the writer's), but they are very rare and they fester in a writer's conscience, making him always more careful. Important mistakes are infinitely rarer. Every writer's mail is full of letters that upbraid him for having made mistakes which he has not made. Some of them come from people who think they know the subject better than he but don't, others from people whose emotions are so engaged that they cannot tolerate the facts. But every writer comes to realize that still more are from people who have not bothered to read him carefully enough to see what he said. They simply have an urge to instruct.

The other trigger any bit of printed matter presses is one that automatically releases a blood lust which never ceases to astonish a writer. Again, don't misunderstand me: I do not mean criticism of one's work. A reader pays a nickel or a dime or a half-dollar for a magazine, or three dollars for a book, and part of what he buys is the right to consider it rotten. But many readers appear to buy as well a license to reconstruct the writer's mind, character, religion, philosophy, politics and opinions on matters totally unrelated to the context. Usually they do so with a heat and violence no editor would permit a writer to use. The first letter I ever got about an article of mine began, "Dear Sir, You are full of red ants." It established a category for me and I have classified as red-ants letters the many hundreds I have had since, that have denounced me on wholly irrelevant grounds, very often with unprintable abuse.

Frequently the trigger releases the energies of extreme bigots, eccentrics, monomaniacs, or even maniacs. The letters they write can be filed in a subdivision of the red-ants category, one for which Elmer Davis once found the right label: he called them Dear-Sir-you-cur letters. Let a writer, however incidentally, mention liquor for instance (and, after all, liquor does exist and people have been drinking it for a long time) and he will get letters vituperating him for plunging weaklings deeper into their vice and for corrupting the innocent young. The same goes for any kind of religious or political or economic idea, however parenthetically alluded to, however small a part of what he has written. But you do not have to allude to anything at all in order to incite that vituperation. Why, a reader will demand in the fiercest words he knows, why have I tragically wasted my time writing about the United Nations, say, or about a new poem? I must surely know, he says, that it is 11.59 P.M. on the eve of Judgment Day, that the world is still to be saved, that I am called on to do my part. The world can be saved even now but only if we make people live on lettuce (or raw meat or turnip juice) exclusively, if we make people understand that the earth is flat, if we abolish zippers or bathtubs or corsets or comic books or vaccination or daylight-saving time. Abandoning all else, I am to join truth's great crusade and triumphantly vindicate turnip juice before midnight strikes. Moreover, a lie has befouled history and brought the world to this pass, the lie that William Shakespeare wrote William Shakespeare's plays — I must assume responsibility and give mankind leave to hope again. Who has laid our distressful country low, who has destroyed the purity of American family life, who has kept the United States from electing a woman

President and thereby assuring world peace, who has led the conspiracy that has prevented the single tax from stamping out poverty or the gospel of deep-breathing from stamping out disease? Only one person in all the world: I . . . or whatever other writer the embattled reader has chanced to come across.

Novelists can protect themselves from some of this irrelevance. If you call a town Bildad instead of New York, Sioux City, or San Diego, you can arrange things to suit yourself and no one can gainsay you. No one can write in derisively that your heroine's address is really that of a glue factory, or angrily that you have got the creek flowing in the wrong direction, or censoriously that the disastrous lightning storm really occurred two days earlier than your book says. But novelists have vocational perils of their own. The legend, "all characters in this book are imaginary and any resemblance to actual persons, living or dead, is purely coincidental" — that legend is wasted. Most readers know it is true but there are always some who will bare their teeth at it. Disregard those who see all novels as *romans à clef*, that is, books which give the lowdown on the novelist's friends and enemies or on public personages. They are like the wise guys who know the inside of politics or baseball or racing, or like the people who can get it for you wholesale. But also there are always a few people, all complete strangers to the novelist, who discover that he had them in mind when he wrote the book, and who write in telling him of their surprise. When they are men they are usually enraged and so berate him for snooping into their private lives or denounce the prejudice that made him misrepresent the purity of their motives. When they are women — I'm sorry to say this, girls, but it's true — they have usually responded to the tender subtlety of his understanding. How, they write, how could you, a stranger, know me so well?

And usually the novelist eats it up. He is an egotist too and, forgetting that in some moods he damns this whole segment of his correspondence, he understands that such letters show how truly fine a writer he is. Has he not made his characters so alive that they embody universal truths? Look, in Grand Rapids, in Tuscaloosa, in Stockton, a woman has found her innermost self expressed by his heroine. Out of his talent he has spoken to the heart's knowledge of itself. Could Thackeray ever do that?

Other letters are less soothing. A novelist writes stories about imaginary people but his characters cannot exist in a vacuum. They have to have occupations. They have to go about the make-believe world as if it were real, they have to do things and see things happening and engage in the manifold activities of life, a good many of which are well beyond the novelist's own experience. He does his best. If one of his characters is a garage mechanic or a wheat farmer or an astronomer, he sweats out all the occupational details he can. But he is interested primarily in the mechanic's emotions, not how he tinkers with a carburetor, and though he may keep the phones of experts ringing he can never be one hundred per cent right. So dozens of mechanics or astronomers who haven't read a novel since 1941 read his and with a kind, forbearing patience or with Dear-Sir-you-fool contempt sit down and tell him how distributor-points really are adjusted or what Saturn really looks like through a telescope. He is glad to learn, in case he may need Saturn again sometime, which is unlikely, but he is writing novels, not technical treatises. What difference does it make, he wonders, if he had Alfred use the wrong kind of wrench? "So few people who can write know anything," Walter Bagehot said. But Bagehot was a writer too and he seemed to get by.

But these are men whose professional pride has been touched and I love them. I don't love the ah-hah! boys — and girls. They get a feeling of superiority to the novelist and score a fine triumph over him, from detecting some implausibility or contradiction that is infinitesimal not only in the novel but anywhere else. On p. 182 you say that in his anxiety Alfred drove his car round a sharp curve at 90 miles an hour — haven't you ever driven a car, you goon? On p. 37 Alfred meets Mariana at the lake under a full moon — that must have been June 20 but the moon wasn't full till June 21. If Mariana is a blonde (see p. 7) she's a fool to wear the shade of red you describe on p. 214. The swallows don't reach Ohio till a week later than you say, the Super Chief does not stop at Red Dog, there is no tide in the Hudson River [there is too, you goon], women were not wearing their hair that way in 1936, p. 300 sounds like Japanese beetles to me and so spraying wouldn't get her anywhere, how did they keep the butter from melting all that time? he couldn't possibly remember Armistice Day for he was only a year old then, you can't see Long's Peak from Denver, how does he get her letter so soon, not even air mail could do it, good God, don't writers ever stop to think and if you can't do simple arithmetic why didn't you work it out with an old alarm clock?

Well, the writer asked for it. Nobody ever asked or petitioned or implored him to write a book. No public demand was ever set up, no horseman galloped through the night to hammer on his door. He did it voluntarily, of his own will. Writing is the most exhibitionistic of trades. The writer climbs up there on a box top, starts yelling and makes every bid he can for public attention. He is exactly like the Dodger of the old sideshows, the man who put his head through a hole in a sheet and let people throw baseballs at him, three for a nickel. When a writer puts his head through that hole he is issuing a general invitation for people to throw things at him. It's naïve of him to hope that all who pay admission will throw roses. There is certain to be a pop bottle or a diseased egg or a dead cat somewhere within reach — he has no legitimate kick if some thoughtful, hard-to-convince person sees it and picks it up.